Access and Equity

Promoting High-Quality Mathematics

in Pre-K–Grade 2

Edited by

Sylvia Celedón-Pattichis
University of New Mexico
Albuquerque, New Mexico

Dorothy Y. White
University of Georgia
Athens, Georgia

Marta Civil
The University of Arizona
Tucson, Arizona

Series Editor
Marta Civil
The University of Arizona
Tucson, Arizona

NATIONAL COUNCIL OF
TEACHERS OF MATHEMATICS

Library of Congress Cataloging-in-Publication Data

Names: Celedon-Pattichis, Sylvia, editor. | White, Dorothy Y., editor. |
  Civil, Marta, editor. | National Council of Teachers of Mathematics.
Title: Access and equity : promoting high quality mathematics in preK-grade 2
  / edited by Sylvia Celedon-Pattichis, University of New Mexico, Albuquerque, New Mexico,
Dorothy Y. White, University of Georgia, Athens, Georgia, Marta Civil, The University of
Arizona, Tucson, Arizona.
Description: Reston, VA : The National Council of Teachers of Mathematics, Inc., [2017] |
Includes bibliographical references. |
Identifiers: LCCN 2017028661 (print) | LCCN 2017040395 (ebook) | ISBN 9781680540086
() | ISBN 9780873539746
Subjects: LCSH: Mathematics--Study and teaching (Preschool)—United States. |
  Mathematics--Study and teaching (Elementary)--United States. |
  Multicultural education--United States. | Educational
equalization—United States.
Classification: LCC QA13 (ebook) | LCC QA13 .A32923 2017 (print) | DDC
  372.7/044--dc23
LC record available at https://lccn.loc.gov/2017028661

The National Council of Teachers of Mathematics supports and advocates for the highest-quality mathematics teaching and learning for each and every student.

Printed in the United States of America

CONTENTS

PREFACE

This book is part of a series that grew from a proposal by the Educational Materials Committee at the National Council of Teachers of Mathematics (NCTM) to develop a collection of books based on the Access and Equity Principle for school mathematics from *Principles to Actions: Ensuring Mathematical Success for All* (NCTM 2014). In embarking on this project, the editors of the different volumes and I looked at previous NCTM publications addressing equity—and at two series in particular: *Mathematics for Every Student: Responding to Diversity*, edited by Carol Malloy (2008–2009), and *Changing the Faces of Mathematics*, edited by Walter Secada (1999–2002). We want to acknowledge these previous efforts, as these series have been an inspiration to our professional trajectories and to our thinking for this current set of books.

As this series, *Access and Equity: Promoting High-Quality Mathematics*, was being developed, a wider discussion on equity was taking place among several professional organizations in mathematics education. In his president's message of September 15, 2016, NCTM President Matt Larson writes, "The NCTM Board has officially reframed its equity work to focus on Access, Equity **and Empowerment** to capture the critical constructs of students' mathematical identities, sense of agency, and social justice" (Larson 2016; emphasis in original). Additionally, the joint position paper *Mathematics Education through the Lens of Social Justice: Acknowledgment, Actions, and Accountability*, by the National Council of Supervisors of Mathematics (NCSM) and TODOS: Mathematics for ALL (NCSM and TODOS 2016), served as a catalyst for this discussion. We hope this series presents a valuable, powerful, and timely contribution to these conversations.

The Access and Equity Principle states, "An excellent mathematics program requires that all students have access to a high-quality mathematics curriculum, effective teaching and learning, high expectations, and the support and resources needed to maximize their learning potential" (NCTM 2014, p. 5). All the books in this series offer strategies and tools to support teachers not only as they implement the Access and Equity Principle but also as they reflect on their students' empowerment. The series is a good companion for the joint position statement mentioned above (NCSM and TODOS 2016). The chapters in each book address a wide range of areas relevant to issues of access and equity in school mathematics, including beliefs about teaching and learning, curriculum aspects, and families and community knowledge as resources for mathematics instruction. They offer concrete examples to address several of the suggested actions listed in the NCSM and TODOS position statement.

This book and the others in this series address access and equity with a focus on diversity (e.g., culture, race, ethnicity, home language or languages, gender, economic status, disability) as an asset to teaching and learning mathematics. Within these diverse settings, the chapters provide examples of (but are not limited to) the following scenarios:

- Students collaboratively engaging in powerful mathematical discussions

- Teachers adapting instruction to meet the needs of all students while maintaining high expectations

- Assessment that takes into account the various ways that students demonstrate their mathematical thinking

- Curriculum that draws on the resources that all students bring to the classroom

- Teachers examining their own beliefs and expectations about teaching and learning

- Tools that encourage teachers to analyze and revise their lessons with an equity lens

- Teachers engaging in school and community partnerships

The four books in this series (Pre-K–grade 2; grades 3–5; grades 6–8; grades 9–12) are aimed primarily at teachers, teacher leaders, and professional developers. The books are research based and practice focused; many of the chapters include classroom teachers as co-authors. In selecting the authors for the chapters, the editors looked for a varied representation in terms of areas of expertise to ensure a balanced series that covers different aspects of access and equity. A common perspective to all authors is a focus on diversity as a resource toward high-quality teaching and learning of mathematics. Such a perspective addresses the overall theme of access, equity, and empowerment through initiatives that are based on a deep respect for the communities with which we work. We learn with them and from them. The authors draw on ideas such as the importance to learn from students' and their families' out-of-school experiences and build on these funds of knowledge (González, Moll, and Amanti

2005) for mathematics teaching and learning (Civil 2007); students' use of home language(s) as a resource in their learning of mathematics (Celedón-Pattichis and Turner 2012; Moschkovich 2013); Ladson-Billings's (1995) criteria for culturally relevant pedagogy in terms of academic success, cultural competence and critical consciousness (p. 160); the need to understand students' mathematical identity (Aguirre, Mayfield-Ingram, and Martin 2013); and an understanding of the sociopolitical nature of mathematics teaching and learning (Gutiérrez 2013; Gutstein 2006).

Specifically, the books in this series aim to support teachers in—

- expanding their thinking about access and equity in mathematics teaching and learning;

- understanding and addressing the obstacles to achieving access and equity;

- exploring productive and unproductive beliefs in relation to access and equity;

- examining the role of expectations in relation to access and equity;

- using mathematically rigorous and challenging tasks with a focus on access and equity;

- learning how to adapt mathematics curriculum materials so that they meet the Access and Equity Principle; and

- developing and sustaining school and community partnerships as fundamental to a commitment to access and equity.

Chapters throughout the series follow the same structure. They start with a practice-based vignette intended to introduce the main message or messages of the chapter. The authors then discuss how they approached the principle of Access and Equity, sharing specific resources and strategies they used so that readers can adapt them to their contexts. The final section of each chapter includes reflection questions or possible actions for readers to consider. This structure makes the books appropriate for individual reading as well as for book club reading with a group of teachers or teacher leaders.

This series would have not been possible without the support and collaboration of many people. I want to thank the Educational Materials Committee at NCTM for giving me the opportunity to develop these books and trusting my judgment in my choice of volume editors and letting us decide how to structure the books. I am also very grateful to Joanne Hodges and Joe Wood for their guidance and patience answering my many questions on NCTM's guidelines for publication and to Julie Schorfheide for her editorial assistance. Most of all, I want to thank the wonderful volume editors, who have worked tirelessly for months not only on the volumes they led but also across the series to make sure that we have a coherent product. Their dedication, professionalism, and knowledge of the field are admirable. I have learned so much from working with them. Finally, the volume editors and I thank the authors who accepted our invitation to contribute. They gave us these rich chapters that underscore their commitment to developing teaching and learning environments grounded on a deep respect for the mathematical thinking of teachers, students, and their families.

Marta Civil, Series Editor

References

Aguirre, Julia, Karen Mayfield-Ingram, and Danny Bernard Martin. *The Impact of Identity in K–8 Mathematics Learning and Teaching: Rethinking Equity-Based Practices.* Reston, Va.: National Council of Teachers of Mathematics, 2013.

Celedón-Pattichis, Sylvia, and Erin E. Turner. "'Explícame tu Respuesta': Supporting the Development of Mathematical Discourse in Emergent Bilingual Kindergarten Students." *Bilingual Research Journal* 35, no. 2 (2012): 197–216.

Civil, Marta. "Building on Community Knowledge: An Avenue to Equity in Mathematics Education." In *Improving Access to Mathematics: Diversity and Equity in the Classroom*, edited by Na'ilah Suad Nasir and Paul Cobb, pp. 105–17. New York: Teachers College Press, 2007.

González, Norma, Luis Moll, and Cathy Amanti. *Funds of Knowledge: Theorizing Practices in Households, Communities and Classrooms.* Mahwah, N.J.: Lawrence Erlbaum, 2005.

Gutiérrez, Rochelle. "The Sociopolitical Turn in Mathematics Education." *Journal for Research in Mathematics Education* 44, no. 1 (2013): 37–68.

Gutstein, Eric. *Reading and Writing the World with Mathematics: Toward a Pedagogy for Social Justice.* New York: Routledge, 2006.

Ladson-Billings, Gloria. "But That's Just Good Teaching! The Case for Culturally Relevant Pedagogy." *Theory into Practice* 34, no. 3 (1995): 159–65.

Larson, Matt. "A Renewed Focus on Access, Equity, and Empowerment." Blog post, September 15, 2016. http://www.nctm.org/News-and-Calendar/Messages-from-the-President/Archive/Matt-Larson/A-Renewed-Focus-on-Access,-Equity,-and-Empowerment/

Moschkovich, Judit. "Principles and Guidelines for Equitable Mathematics Teaching Practices and Materials for English Language Learners." *Journal of Urban Mathematics Education* 6, no. 1 (2013): 45–57.

National Council of Supervisors of Mathematics and TODOS: Mathematics for ALL (NCSM and TODOS). *Mathematics Education through the Lens of Social Justice: Acknowledgment, Actions, and Accountability.* Joint Position Paper. 2016.

National Council of Teachers of Mathematics (NCTM). *Principles to Actions: Ensuring Mathematics Success for All.* Reston, Va.: NCTM, 2014.

Introduction

Sylvia Celedón-Pattichis, *University of New Mexico*
Dorothy Y. White, *University of Georgia*
Marta Civil, *The University of Arizona*

Before entering school, young children explore the beginnings of mathematical ideas and processes. Children engage in counting, sorting, and classifying objects; noticing patterns and shapes; and other mathematics concepts through play and daily activities (Baroody 2004; Clements et al. 1999; Ginsburg, Klein, and Starkey 1998; Wager 2013; Wager and Parks 2014). The importance of a strong early childhood mathematics education for later learning is well documented (Duncan et al. 2007; NAEYC and NCTM 2002/2010; Watts et al. 2014). In addition, research indicates that once children enter kindergarten and primary grades, they can engage in more complex problem solving using operations, including multiplication and division (Carpenter et al. 1999). These findings have included young Latina/o children engaging in similar mathematics problem solving when they are given the opportunity to do so (Turner and Celedón-Pattichis 2011; Turner et al. 2009).

Principles to Actions: Ensuring Mathematical Success for All (NCTM 2014) states, "Effective mathematics instruction leverages students' culture, conditions, and language to support and enhance mathematics learning" (p. 63). Although ample research indicates that young children have the capacity to explore mathematical ideas in their social and physical environments and to solve more complex mathematics problems in their daily activities, teachers and parents often underestimate this capacity and tend to pay more attention to language rather than to mathematics (Cannon and Ginsburg 2008; Carpenter et al. 1999). In a joint 2002 position statement, the National Association for the Education of Young Children (NAEYC) and NCTM recommended that teachers "actively introduce mathematical concepts, methods, and language through a range of appropriate experiences and teaching strategies" (p. 9). Coupled with this recommendation is the need for early childhood teachers to engage in ongoing learning, teamwork, and planning to develop a coherent mathematics curriculum for the early childhood years.

In *Mathematics Learning in Early Childhood: Paths Toward Excellence and Equity*, the National Research Council delineated several recommendations regarding mathematics learning in early childhood settings (NRC 2009). One recommendation is that early childhood classrooms focus on developing two mathematics strands: number concepts, which includes whole numbers, operations, and relations; and geometry, spatial relations, and measurement, with more time devoted to number concepts. A second recommendation is that "all early childhood programs . . . provide high-quality mathematics curricula and instruction" (NRC 2009, p. 3), a statement that echoes the Access and Equity Principle in *Principles to Actions* (NCTM 2014). A third recommendation is that early childhood programs form collaborations between family and community programs to promote mathematics learning.

Several studies have looked at young children's out-of-school mathematical practices from a sociocultural perspective (e.g., Street, Baker, and Tomlin 2005; Taylor 2009; Tudge and Doucet 2004). As Street, Baker, and Tomlin wrote, "The research, based on a representation of mathematics as social, has revealed the importance of teachers building on students' interests, experience, knowledge of mathematics and drawing on home based funds of knowledge of mathematics" (p. 167). The findings point to the importance of using pedagogical approaches that draw from contexts that are familiar and of interest to students. These pedagogical approaches are particularly important in low-income and linguistically and culturally diverse communities where children's everyday experiences and knowledge bases may look different from the middle-class practices and norms often expected or assumed by schools. Therefore, teachers must engage in culturally responsive pedagogies that use "the cultural knowledge, prior experiences, frames of reference, and performance styles of ethnically diverse students to make learning encounters more relevant to and effective for them" (Gay 2000, p. 29).

Studies on emergent bilinguals and mathematics point to the need for teachers to draw from students' culture and home language(s) as intellectual resources to access mathematics concepts (Celedón-Pattichis and Turner 2012; Moschkovich 2007; Turner and Celedón-Pattichis 2011; Turner et al. 2009). Similar to García and Kleifgen (2010), we use the term *emergent bilinguals* to take a stance that students not only need to develop English as a second language but also need to maintain their home language(s). Teaching practices that are effective for working with emergent bilinguals include framing problem solving around telling and sharing authentic, storytelling conversations, inviting students to share experiences to co-construct these stories, and drawing from familiar ways of talking and negotiating meaning (Delgado-Gaitan 1987; Villenas and Moreno 2001). Teachers also alternate between closed and open-ended questions to develop students' everyday and mathematics discourse, position students as competent problem solvers by supporting them to explain their mathematical thinking, and make connections across multimodal representations. Most important, teachers advocate for emergent bilinguals. This advocacy takes the form of providing access to the home language(s) and intervening to ensure that students have placements that reflect their mathematical performance rather than their English language proficiency.

From this brief overview of the research field and recommendations for early childhood mathematics, we highlight the following four points:

- Children as young as prekindergarten age, including culturally and linguistically diverse students, can engage in challenging mathematical problem solving, and their capacity to do so is often underestimated.

- There are important aspects to consider as young children make a transition from home to school, including English language development, particularly with emergent bilinguals.

- There is a need to consider the role of families, especially families of immigrant origin for whom this may be their first experience with schools in their new country.

- Pedagogical practices should draw on culturally relevant/responsive teaching that builds on students' mathematical cultures and strengths.

This book addresses the aforementioned points across three themes: creating supportive mathematics discourse communities for young children, including emergent bilinguals; bridging community (informal, family, home) knowledge and mathematics classrooms (schools); and engaging teachers in critical reflection with professional development tools. Some of the themes cut across several chapters, as described in the following sections.

Creating Supportive Mathematics Discourse Communities for Young Children

Teachers empower students through critical decisions they make in the classroom, particularly in how they plan to support young children, including emergent bilinguals, to communicate their mathematical thinking in the classroom. Research has indicated the importance of engaging and supporting young emergent bilinguals in explaining their mathematical thinking using their language(s) as a resource(s) (Celedón-Pattichis and Turner 2012; Moschkovich 2007; Musanti and Celedón-Pattichis 2014; Willey 2010). An important component of creating a mathematics discourse community includes the use of multimodal representations. Teachers place importance upon *how* students represent their solutions (Chval and Khisty 2009), whether using spoken or written words, pictures, and/or symbols (chapters 1–5). Nonverbal communication, such as gestures (Fernandes and McLeman 2012) and keystrokes on a calculator (Chval and Khisty 2009), is also part of multimodal representation. The use of technology tools is presented as a multimodal approach to support students in developing number fluency (chapter 5). A progression of how emergent bilinguals develop a second language and communicate mathematical thinking, how they use multimodal representations, and how teachers position students as competent problem solvers is described in Celedón-Pattichis and Ramirez (2012) and illustrated in chapters 2, 3, and 4.

Bridging Community (Informal, Family, Home) Knowledge and Mathematics Classrooms (Schools)

Several of the chapters in this book address the importance of bridging home and school by connecting to children's out-of-school experiences to develop rich mathematical learning experiences (chapters 2, 3, 8, and 10); describing ways to interact with families about mathematics teaching and learning; and emphasizing the need for an authentic two-way dialogue between home and school (Civil 2002) (chapters 6 and 7). "Funds of knowledge," a fundamental concept behind the majority of these chapters, refers to the "historically accumulated and culturally developed bodies of knowledge and skills essential for household or individual functioning and wellbeing" (Moll et al. 2005, p. 72). In particular, many of the chapters in this book provide specific illustrations of how to develop mathematics learning experiences that build on the funds of knowledge of students and their families. In so doing, the authors reject the all-too-often pervasive deficit views on low-income, nondominant communities, and instead capitalize on the richness of resources in students, families, and communities.

Engaging Teachers in Critical Reflection with Professional Development Tools

According to Cranton, "becoming a better teacher includes questioning and thinking critically about one's own practice" (1996, p. 2). In recent years, mathematics education researchers have studied the influence of teachers' professional noticing of students' mathematical thinking on issues of equity. These scholars have found that improving students' access to mathematics can be enhanced when teachers notice children's participation in the classroom (Wager 2014) and become more aware of the relationship between what they notice and their dispositions toward equity (Hand 2012). Many of the chapters in this book illustrate the ways in which teachers attend to students' ways of thinking and doing mathematics and reflect on their pedagogical practices and decisions (chapters 1 and 4). In some specific chapters, teachers have used tools such as technology to support the ways they notice student thinking (chapters 5 and 9).

The chapters in this book showcase the power of embracing the knowledge, cultures, and linguistic strengths of every child. They provide counterexamples of the deficit views often voiced about what historically underrepresented students are capable of doing in mathematics classrooms. In other words,

> [t]hese good beginnings reflect all the characteristics of good early childhood education: deep understanding of children's development and learning; a strong community of teachers, families, and children; research-based knowledge of early childhood curriculum and teaching practices; continuous assessment in the service of children's learning; and an abiding respect for young children's families, cultures, and communities. (NAEYC and NCTM 2002, p. 13)

Organization of This Book

The first five chapters illustrate different avenues for engaging young children, including emergent bilinguals, in mathematical talk and multimodal representations in pre-K–grade 2. These five chapters share an emphasis on problem solving that builds on the resources that children bring to the classroom and on the teachers' high expectations for the students' learning. The chapters also differ: One uses literature and statistical data that are meaningful to children, another draws from dramatic play with young children in prekindergarten, the third draws from problem posing as a way to deepen children's understanding of basic operations, the fourth positions students as actors and narrators to participate in a mathematics discourse community using a growth mindset, and the fifth describes how an app can be used to engage first-grade students in multimodal ways of developing mathematical thinking, particularly with counting and place value.

A common theme among the next three chapters is the connections that can be made between home and community knowledge and mathematics classrooms. The first chapter illustrates collaboration between parents and a school and describes three approaches that can be used to engage families, students, and teachers in critical advocacy for teaching mathematics for understanding using a reform-based curriculum. The second chapter challenges traditional views of engaging families in young children's learning of mathematics and provides recommendations for take-home activities that create paths for communication between families and teachers. The third chapter presents two frameworks generated by teachers' reflections and discussions that relate to students' mathematical thinking outside of school and shows how teachers can use problem context categories to expand the way they pose word problems to build place-value understanding.

The last two chapters focus on engaging teachers in critical reflection with professional development tools to ensure high-quality mathematics for each and every student. The first chapter focuses on using tools such as "mathematical thinking conversations," videos from classroom activities, and software to engage teachers in meaningful professional development in early childhood mathematics education. The second chapter provides tools that engage teachers in making connections between students' home and community knowledge and their mathematics instructional planning.

Synopsis of Chapters

In chapter 1, "'What Color Are Our Feet?' Empowering Prekindergarteners' Statistical Reasoning through Opportunities to Create, Discuss, and Own Visual Representations," Theodore Chao and DeAndrea Jones present several weeks of activities to empower prekindergarteners, ages four to five. The authors illustrate how students created, organized, interpreted, and used statistical data about themselves in ways meaningful to them. When the children from this low-income school played with, experimented with, and analyzed multiple structures for eliciting and representing data, they engaged in meaningful discussions about their mathematical thinking and took ownership of the data, and each had a voice in the ensuing classroom discourse. The series of activities detailed in this chapter, co-created by the teacher and the children, showcase equitable and accessible ways for young children to communicate their mathematical thinking through data as they create unique graphs, songs, and diagrams.

In chapter 2, "'Tengo toda la receta acá': Developing Mathematical Agency in Young Emerging Bilinguals," Anne Karabon, Giselle Martinez Negrette, Michelle Smith, and Anita Wager provide evidence of culturally and developmentally responsive mathematics teaching practices that support young emerging bilinguals with opportunities to engage in rich mathematics that provide agency. Mathematics is present in the dramatic play area when the children are encouraged to write their own recipes or to put prices on the food served in their "Mexican restaurant." In all of these spaces, the "math talk" (90 percent of which is in Spanish) brings together language and mathematical knowledge that supports the children's identities as Latina/o learners and doers of mathematics. Smith's teaching practices communicate to these young children a powerful message of agency in mathematics that positively affects their learning process. Looking at these teaching practices can provide insight into how mathematical knowledge can be part of the daily activities of children at a very young age. It also shows how teachers can provide access to meaningful mathematics learning opportunities, have high expectations, support the development of children's mathematical identity, have an assets based (growth) mindset, and build on children's cultural and linguistic resources.

In "¿Qué observamos aquí? ¿Qué preguntas tienen?: Problem Solving in Ms. Bustillos's Second-Grade Bilingual Classroom," Erin Turner and Lus Bustillos present examples from a second-grade classroom with emergent bilinguals engaging in meaningful problem-solving activities. The authors illustrate how problem posing not only enhances understanding of basic operations but also fosters a greater connection to mathematics when the context is relevant and meaningful to children's lives. The chapter describes three specific features of problem posing that advance equity and access to mathematics for each and every student, and specifically emergent bilinguals. These features include the potential of problem posing to deepen student understanding of basic operations; position students' home, cultural, and community-based knowledge as a resource both for creating and solving mathematics problems; and provide context-rich opportunities for emergent bilinguals to use and develop mathematics language.

In chapter 4, "Supporting English Language Learners in a Discourse Community," Nora Ramirez and Socorro Tapetillo draw from ideas of a growth mindset to highlight a second-grade teacher, Ms. Tapetillo, who engages all English language learners in mathematical discourse. Trying an unusual approach, she gave her students an opportunity to become actors and narrators. Socorro shares many surprises, describes student growth both in language and self-confidence that resulted from students' participation in a theatrical presentation, and discusses the effect of this activity on students' participation in a mathematical discourse community. In addition, the authors share examples of how a growth mindset permeated Ms. Tapetillo's classroom, in particular students' mathematical approaches to learning, including communicating to other students their understanding, concretely, visually, and in words, both written and oral.

In "Equity and Access to the Complexity of Number: A Multimodal, Digital Approach," Rebecca Cohen, Sean Chorney, and Nathalie Sinclair describe the use of a touchscreen app, TouchCounts, with first graders who faced challenges developing number fluency. Since this technology tool offers a multimodal approach to early number, including visual, aural, gestural, tactile, and symbolic modes of making and manipulating number, the authors focus explicitly on how these different modalities enabled children to employ multiple means to use their fingers and gestures to engage more proficiently in counting, skip-counting, doubling, subitizing, and decomposing, as well as in attending to place value. The authors also highlight the way in which working with ordinal aspects of number, that is, attending to the relation between symbols, may provide significant support to number sense development, particularly as children begin to work more extensively with operations.

The sixth chapter, "Developing Advocacy for Equitable Approaches to Teaching Mathematics from Within," by Maura Varley Gutiérrez and Georgette Abouattier Blay, describes a multifaceted, schoolwide approach to creating a culture of collaboration among students, teachers, and families to ensure the success of a reform-based mathematics curriculum in a diverse, urban, language-immersion elementary school. The chapter focuses primarily on three family engagement efforts, with practical application within classrooms or schoolwide. In the first, called Open Classroom, families are given an overview of teaching mathematics for understanding and then are invited to spend time observing a mathematics lesson of their child and to debrief with teachers and administrators. The second, Family Math Workshops, consists of content-based sessions for families in which they explore clusters of content standards by grade level. They observe students engaging in reform-based mathematics curricular activities or watch videos of students using multiple strategies to solve problems in order to understand the progression of strategy development. The final effort, Family Meetings, is a strategy-based assessment system involving problem-solving interviews, used to inform families of growth in strategy development on key grade-level skills. The chapter includes descriptions of the ways in which these efforts have led to critical student, teacher, and parent advocacy for teaching mathematics for understanding for all.

In chapter 7, "Creating Inclusive Opportunities for Family Involvement in Mathematics," Rachel Monette and Amy Noelle Parks discuss ways of engaging families in mathematical activities with their children without requiring attendance at after-school events. For example, sending home small sets of blocks, materials for cooking activities, or puzzles can promote mathematical conversations in the home. Take-home activities can also allow teachers to learn more about rich mathematical practices in children's home lives that might otherwise go unnoticed. By inviting caregivers to send back notes or even to email digital photos (e.g., taken on phones), teachers can learn more about how children use mathematics in their homes and can use these artifacts from the home as launch points for mathematical discussions in the classroom. In addition, teachers can encourage families to explore particular mathematical ideas with the materials, such as finding as many ways as possible to make a square with a small set of blocks. Experiences such as these can help caregivers understand mathematics concepts from the Common Core State Standards, such as composing and decomposing, that might otherwise be difficult to understand. In this way, take-home activities create paths of communication between families and teachers, as well as positive feelings about mathematics.

In chapter 8, "Using the Mathematics They Know and Maximizing the Mathematics They Don't: Making Contexts Work," Edd Taylor presents two useful frameworks that came out of teacher reflections and discussions of their efforts to draw on students' informal knowledge. The first describes four categories of connecting that have higher and lower relation to students' mathematical thinking outside of school, as well as different levels of student participation. Teachers can consider the ways in which their lessons fall within these categories, and when certain categories might be more useful. This framework also addresses the ways in which these connections are related to the types of manipulatives that might be chosen, particularly in building number sense and base-ten/place-value understanding. The second framework includes problem context categories that can support teachers in expanding the ways they use word problems (e.g., for inclusion, funds of knowledge, cultural knowledge). This chapter will support teachers in using strategies and constructing lessons that should lead to more equitable learning for all students.

In chapter 9, "Math Thinking Conversations: A Tool for Engaging Teachers and Children in Deep Mathematical Practice," Cassie Freeman, Herbert Ginsburg, Haifa Bautista, and Colleen Uscianowski describe their collaboration, including the use of videos of classroom activities to guide the professional development sessions, and the ways that the teachers have changed their practice as a result of what they learned about their children. A guiding principle of this collaboration was ensuring that all children at PrePrep (part of New York City's universal prekindergarten program) receive challenging, engaging mathematics instruction. In order to achieve this goal, the authors visited the school twice a month for observations and conversations with children, which they video recorded for use in the twice-monthly professional development sessions. During these sessions, teachers extended their practice of thinking conversations by focusing on mathematics centers, mathematics storybooks, and the use of interactive software to provide students with appropriate challenges. Further, teachers brought their own interests and creativity to the collaboration, recording their own mathematical thinking conversations and suggesting particular mathematics content to develop their expertise. The authors hope this collaboration can serve as a model for long-term involvement between universities and schools to improve access to high-quality early childhood mathematics education.

Finally, chapter 10, "Connecting Children's Mathematical Thinking with Children's Backgrounds, Knowledge, and Experiences in Mathematics Instruction," by Tonya Gau Bartell, Mary Foote, Amy Roth McDuffie, Erin Turner, Julia Aguirre, and Corey Drake, includes tools teachers can use to build connections between home and community resources in ways that honor children's multiple knowledge bases in their mathematics instructional planning. Using two vignettes of teachers engaging with children's communities and designing mathematically rich problem-solving experiences that incorporate knowledge both of children's mathematical thinking and of their home and community experiences (one vignette set in grade 2 and one in kindergarten), the authors put forth suggestions for activities teachers can engage in (e.g., getting-to-know-you interview; community walk), based on the authors' research in the TEACH MATH project. Working to build such connections can support a strength-based perspective of students, families, and communities that supports children's learning of mathematics.

References

Baroody, Arthur J. "The Role of Psychological Research in the Development of Early Childhood Mathematics Standards." In *Engaging Young Children in Mathematics: Standards for Early Childhood Mathematics Education*, edited by Douglas H. Clements, Julie Sarama, and Ann-Marie DiBiase, pp. 149–72. Mahwah, N.J.: Lawrence Erlbaum, 2004.

Cannon, Joanna, and Herbert P. Ginsburg. "'Doing the Math': Maternal Beliefs about Early Mathematics Versus Language Learning." *Early Education and Development* 19, no. 2 (2008): 238–60.

Carpenter, Thomas, Elizabeth Fennema, Megan L. Franke, Linda Levi, and Susan B. Empson. *Children's Mathematics: Cognitively Guided Instruction.* Portsmouth, N.H.: Heinemann; Reston, Va.: National Council of Teachers of Mathematics, 1999.

Celedón-Pattichis, Sylvia, and Nora G. Ramirez. *Beyond Good Teaching: Advancing Mathematics Education for ELLs.* Reston, Va: National Council of Teachers of Mathematics, 2012.

Celedón-Pattichis, Sylvia, and Erin E. Turner. "'Explícame tu Respuesta': Supporting the Development of Mathematical Discourse in Emergent Bilingual Kindergarten Students." *Bilingual Research Journal* 35, no. 2 (2012): 197–216.

Chval, Kathryn B., and Lena L. Khisty. "Bilingual Latino Students, Writing and Mathematics: A Case Study of Successful Teaching and Learning." In *Multilingualism in Mathematics*

Classrooms: Global Perspectives, edited by Richard Barwell, pp. 128–44. Buffalo, N.Y.: Multilingual Matters, 2009.

Civil, Marta. "Culture and Mathematics: A Community Approach." *Journal of Intercultural Studies* 23, no. 2 (2002): 133–48.

Clements, Douglas H., Sudha Swaminathan, Mary-Anne Zeitler Hannibal, and Julie Sarama. "Young Children's Concepts of Shape." *Journal for Research in Mathematics Education* 30, no. 2 (1999): 192–212.

Cranton, Patricia. *Professional Development as Transformative Learning: New Perspectives for Teachers of Adults.* San Francisco, Calif.: Jossey-Bass, 1996.

Delgado-Gaitan, Concha. "Traditions and Transitions in the Learning Process of Mexican Children: An Ethnographic View." In *Interpretive Ethnography of Education: At Home and Abroad*, edited by George Spindler and Louise Spindler, pp. 333–59. Hillsdale, N.J.: Erlbaum, 1987.

Duncan, Greg J., Chantelle J. Dowsett, Amy Claessens, Katherine Magnuson, Aletha C. Huston, Pamela Klebanov, Linda S. Pagani, et al. "School Readiness and Later Achievement." *Developmental Psychology* 43, no. 6 (2007): 1428–46.

Fernandes, Anthony, and Laura McLeman. "Interpreting and Using Gestures of English Language Learners in Mathematics Teaching." *Teaching Equity and Excellence in Mathematics* 4, no. 1 (2012): 16–23.

García, Ofelia, and Jo Anne Kleifgen. *Educating Emergent Bilinguals: Policies, Programs, and Practices for English Language Learners.* New York: Teachers College Press, 2010.

Gay, Geneva. *Culturally Responsive Teaching: Theory, Research, and Practice.* New York: Teachers College Press, 2000.

Ginsburg, Herbert P., Alice Klein, and Prentice Starkey. "The Development of Children's Mathematical Thinking: Connecting Research with Practice." In *Handbook of Child Psychology, Volume 4: Child Psychology in Practice*, edited by William Damon, Irving E. Sigel, and K. Anne Renninger, pp. 401–76. New York: John Wiley & Sons, 1998.

Hand, Victoria. "Seeing Culture and Power in Mathematical Learning: Toward a Model of Equitable Instruction." *Educational Studies in Mathematics* 80, no. 1–2 (2012): 233–47.

Moll, Luis C., Cathy Amanti, Deborah Neff, and Norma González. "Funds of Knowledge for Teaching: Using a Qualitative Approach to Connect Homes and Classrooms." In *Funds of Knowledge: Theorizing Practice in Households, Communities, and Classrooms*, edited by Norma González, Luis Moll, and Cathy Amanti, pp. 71–87. Mahwah, N.J.: Lawrence Erlbaum, 2005.

Moschkovich, Judit N. "Examining Mathematical Discourse Practices." *For the Learning of Mathematics* 27, no. 1 (2007): 24–30.

Musanti, Sandra I., and Sylvia Celedón-Pattichis. "Promising Pedagogical Practices for Emergent Bilinguals in Kindergarten: Towards a Mathematics Discourse Community." *Journal of Multilingual Education Research* 4, no. 1 (2014): 39–62.

National Association for the Education of Young Children (NAEYC) and National Council of Teachers of Mathematics (NCTM). *Early Childhood Mathematics: Promoting Good Beginnings.* Joint position statement. 2002. Updated 2010. http://www.naeyc.org/files/naeyc/file/positions/psmath.pdf.

National Council of Teachers of Mathematics (NCTM). *Principles to Actions: Ensuring Mathematics Success for All.* Reston, Va.: NCTM, 2014.

National Research Council. *Mathematics Learning in Early Childhood: Paths Toward Excellence and Equity.* Edited by Christopher T. Cross, Taniesha A. Woods, and Heidi Schweingruber. Committee on Early Childhood Mathematics, Center for Education, Division of Behavioral and Social Sciences and Education. Washington, D.C.: National Academies Press, 2009.

Street, Brian, Dave Baker, and Alison Tomlin. *Navigating Numeracy: Home/School Numeracy Practices.* Dordrecht, The Netherlands: Springer, 2005.

Taylor, Edd V. "The Purchasing Practice of Low-Income Students: The Relationship to Mathematical Development." *Journal of the Learning Sciences* 18, no. 3 (2009): 370–415. doi:10.1080/10508400903013462

Tudge, Jonathan R. H., and Fabienne Doucet. "Early Mathematical Experiences: Observing Young Black and White Children's Everyday Activities." *Early Childhood Research Quarterly* 19, no. 1 (2004): 21–39. doi:10.1016/j.ecresq.2004.01.007

Turner, Erin E., and Sylvia Celedón-Pattichis. "Mathematical Problem Solving among Latina/o Kindergartners: An Analysis of Opportunities to Learn." *Journal of Latinos and Education* 10, no. 2 (2011): 146–69.

Turner, Erin E., Sylvia Celedón-Pattichis, Mary Marshall, and Alan Tennison. "'*Fíjense amorcitos, les voy a contar una historia*': The Power of Story to Support Solving and Discussing Mathematical Problems with Latino/a Kindergarten Students." In *Mathematics for Every Student: Responding to Diversity in Grades Pre-K–5*, edited by Dorothy Y. White and Julie Sliva Spitzer, pp. 23–41. Reston, Va.: National Council of Teachers of Mathematics, 2009.

Villenas, Sofía, and Melissa Moreno. "To *valerse por si misma* between Race, Capitalism, and Patriarchy: Latina Mother-Daughter Pedagogies in North Carolina." *Journal of Qualitative Studies in Education* 14, no. 5 (2001): 671–87.

Wager, Anita A. "Practices That Support Mathematics Learning in a Play-Based Classroom." In *Reconceptualizing Early Mathematics Learning,* edited by Lyn D. English and Joanne T. Mulligan, pp. 163–81. Dordrecht, The Netherlands: Springer, 2013.

Wager, Anita A. "Noticing Children's Participation Insights into Teacher Positionality toward Equitable Mathematics Pedagogy." *Journal for Research in Mathematics Education* 45, no. 3 (2014): 312–50.

Wager, Anita, and Amy Noelle Parks. "Learning Mathematics Through Play." In *SAGE Handbook of Play and Learning in Early Childhood,* edited by Elizabeth Brooker, Mindy Blaise, and Susan Edwards, pp. 216–27. London: Sage Publications, 2014.

Watts, Tyler W., Greg J. Duncan, Robert S. Siegler, and Pamela E. Davis-Kean. "What's Past Is Prologue: Relations between Early Mathematics Knowledge and High School Achievement." *Educational Researcher* 43, no. 7 (2014): 352–60.

Willey, Craig. "Teachers Developing Mathematics Discourse Communities with Latinas/os." In *Proceedings of the 32nd Annual Meeting of the North American Chapter of the International Group for the Psychology of Mathematics Education*, edited by Patricia Brosnan, Diane B. Erchick, and Lucia Flevares, pp. 530–38. Columbus: The Ohio State University, 2010.

CHAPTER 1

"What Color Are Our Feet?"

Empowering Prekindergarteners' Statistical Reasoning through Opportunities to Create, Discuss, and Own Visual Representations

Theodore Chao, *The Ohio State University*

DeAndrea Jones, *Weinland Park Elementary School, Columbus (Ohio) City Schools*

DeAndrea Jones, a veteran prekindergarten teacher at an urban public school serving a low-income and historically African American community, finishes reading Dr. Seuss's *The Foot Book* (1968) to her classroom of fifteen to twenty children, aged four to five. *The Foot Book* details variations in feet through whimsical rhymes: "Left foot, Right foot, Feet, Feet, Feet, How many, many feet you meet" (Seuss 1968, pp. 8–9). Jones asks the children to look at their shoes and the other shoes in class: What do they notice? As children come up with multiple ways to describe their shoes (e.g., laces or no laces, shoe color), Jones steers the conversation toward organizing what they notice in a way everyone can see. After discussion about various ways to organize the feet, one child asks if they can create a poster of all the feet in the classroom.

"I like that idea!" exclaims Jones, taking up this suggestion and rolling out some butcher paper. Jones then elicits ideas about how to create and organize data about classmates' feet onto the butcher paper. Children come up with various solutions, many of them focused on stepping on the paper. One child suggests stepping in paint first, then walking on the butcher paper. "OK, let's do it," says Jones, directing her assistant teachers to prepare paint and help children remove their shoes and socks. As the children excitedly paint their feet, Jones asks, "How will we know whose feet is whose on the paper?" One child suggests that boys paint their feet one color and girls paint their feet another color.

Another child extends this idea, saying, "Boys on one side, and girls on the other side." Jones takes up these ideas, drawing a line down the middle of the butcher paper. The children line up, paint their feet, and make a footprint onto either side of the butcher paper (with help from the assistant teachers). As the paint dries and children clean off their feet, Jones gathers children around the poster and asks what they notice (see fig. 1.1).

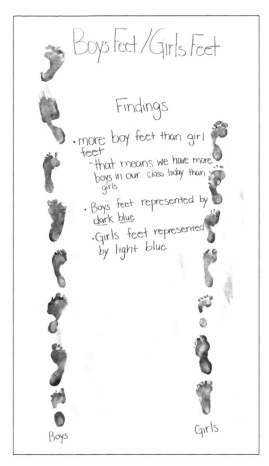

Fig. 1.1. The prekindergarten children's two-column chart of their feet

One child says, "We can count boys' feet and girls' feet." Jones takes up this contribution, writing, "Findings" in the middle of the poster. She hangs up the poster on the front wall and asks children to count the feet. A child says, "There's more boys' feet than girls' feet."

"How did you figure that out?" asks Jones.

"The boys' feet got 8. The girls' feet got 7," answers the child. Jones records the students' findings on the poster.

One week later, when children revisit the chart, a child shares that while the foot chart shows boys and girls, she wished everyone could have chosen their own color. Other children agree; they also wanted to choose the color of their feet. Jones goes to the whiteboard, writing down all the colors children say they would like to paint their feet. The children, eager to paint their feet their chosen color, start removing their shoes and socks. "Freeze," Jones instructs. "How should we organize our data?"

One child says they should make lines like the boys vs. girls chart. Another child says they should make a table. One child asks if they can do a circle of colors. Other children agree with the circle idea, and Jones solicits more information: "What do you mean by a circle? Can you show me?" One child draws a circle with her hands, showing different pieces with different colors, which Jones revoices as a "pie chart."

At this point, Theodore Chao, who was observing this lesson as a mathematics education researcher, steps in to suggest that creating a pie chart by hand might be too complicated for prekindergarteners because of the circular angle measurements and percentages involved. Chao suggests a histogram representation. Jones agrees—a pie chart might be too complex. But the children keep insisting on circle graph. So Jones shrugs her shoulders and says, "I guess we're making a pie chart."

The assistant teachers help children paint their feet while Jones labels the butcher paper "Pie Chart" and draws a big circle. Children, one a time, make a footprint in the circle. Jones organizes all sixteen children as Yellow, Green, Dark Blue, Pink, Blue, and Black, asking children choosing the same color to step in the same section of the pie chart (see fig. 1.2). As children clean up, Jones asks children what conclusions they can make from their pie chart. One child notices that pink is the most popular color and yellow is the least popular color. Jones asks the children to verify this observation, then writes it on the chart. Jones hangs the chart on the wall for children to examine over the next week.

Fig. 1.2. The pie chart children made to organize and analyze the color
of their feet

Making a Commitment to Access and Equity

In *Principles to Actions: Ensuring Mathematical Success for All* (NCTM 2014), NCTM
explicitly frames Access and Equity as the first principle for successful mathematics
teaching and learning. In the vignette that opens this chapter, Jones centers her
children's explorations on this principle, helping "all students have access to a high-
quality mathematics curriculum, effective teaching and learning, high expectations,
and the support and resources needed to maximize their learning potential"
(NCTM 2014, p. 5). During these evolving activities, Jones and Chao watched as
prekindergarteners took ownership of their mathematical discussions around
organizing and creating graphical representations of the data they generated.
Jones routinely gave her children the power to steer the conversation or activity,
positioning herself along the learning experience with her children. This approach
also meant sometimes abandoning learning goals (i.e., children would create
histograms) so the activities would go where children wanted. Jones was able to
make these activities meaningful because of the ways she incorporated principles
of access and equity.

First, Jones positioned all her children as capable of mathematical thinking,
echoing that "mathematics ability is a function of opportunity, experience, and

effort—not of innate intelligence. Mathematics teaching and learning cultivate mathematics abilities. All students are capable of participating and achieving in mathematics, and all deserve support to achieve at the highest levels" (NCTM 2014, p. 63). The classroom discussions were open to each of Jones's children, and the norms of the classroom made each child feel welcome to participate and explore mathematics as valid contributors (see chapter 3). Jones trusted her students to guide her through creating the boys vs. girls foot chart and the foot color pie chart; every child in her class participated in thinking about and physically took part in creating the charts. Through Jones's interactions, each child, regardless of background, felt capable of sophisticated mathematical thinking:

> All students are capable of making sense of and persevering in solving challenging mathematics problems and should be expected to do so. Many more students, regardless of gender, ethnicity, and socioeconomic status, need to be given the support, confidence, and opportunities to reach much higher levels of mathematical success and interest. (NCTM 2014, p. 64)

Second, Jones expected her children to engage in challenging mathematical tasks: "Effective teaching practices (e.g., engaging students with challenging tasks, discourse, and open-ended problem solving) have the potential to open up greater opportunities for higher-order thinking and for raising the mathematics achievement of all students, including poor and low-income students" (NCTM 2014, p. 63). Jones expected her children to problem solve and figure out a way to represent their data without telling them or modeling for them what to do, opening up opportunities for higher-order thinking, something not often expected of prekindergarteners. When the children chose the circle graph representation, Jones knew this might be too challenging, yet she allowed it because it was an opportunity to engage her students with a challenging task.

Third, Jones's teaching espouses the belief that "persistent and unacceptable gaps narrow and ultimately disappear when all students have access to rigorous, high-quality mathematics, taught by teachers who not only understand mathematics but also understand and appreciate learners' social and cultural contexts in meaningful ways" (NCTM 2014, p. 65). Jones treats her classroom as a community in which social and cultural knowledge is built over time. In this example, Jones used *The Foot Book* (Seuss 1968), a class favorite, as a social context to orchestrate an open-ended mathematics activity. Jones also routinely builds her activities off books, songs, and stories that children share from their families, homes, and communities (see chapters 8 and 10). This vignette showcases Jones's commitment to access and equity for her children through high-quality and challenging mathematics teaching.

Advancing Access and Equity

Advancing access and equity in the prekindergarten and early elementary classroom involves adhering to a number of teaching beliefs and practices connecting to *Principles to Actions* (NCTM 2014). Holding children to high standards of mathematical achievement and challenging children with open-ended tasks are part of what makes Jones a dynamic prekindergarten teacher. But beyond these expectations sit a number of subtle teaching dispositions that Jones uses to create opportunities for her prekindergarteners to learn, engage, and "do" mathematics that comes from their own experiences. In Jones's classroom, the concept of "access and equity" involves the following dispositions toward learning:

- Play. Young children learn and reason mathematically through play (Parks 2015; see chapters 2 and 7). Creating opportunities for all children to play and to create mathematical meaning through their play allows children to notice and construct mathematical ideas as they interact with multiple representations.

- Community. Young children need to feel that they belong, that they are supported, and that they are safe (Aguirre, Mayfield-Ingram, and Martin 2013). These assurances open up opportunities for them to engage in mathematics, suggest creative ideas, and ask questions that their curiosity prompts.

- Voice. All children should have a voice in which they can say or talk about what they notice, knowing someone will listen intently to what they are saying (Gutstein 2007; Turner et al. 2016).

Jones's Approach to Access and Equity

First, Jones's classroom focuses heavily on children's collaboration; the class is a community where all voices are heard. This approach connects to the community tenets of the Access and Equity Principle:

> Classroom environments that foster a sense of community that allows students to express their mathematical ideas—together with norms that expect students to communicate their mathematical thinking to their peers and teacher, both orally and in writing, using the language of mathematics—positively affect participation and engagement among all students. (NCTM 2014, p. 66)

In previous years, Jones had children create individual histograms based on sorting and counting different colors from a random sample of multicolored cereal (such as Kellogg's Froot Loops.) Using a pre-created chart, the children colored one appropriate box for each cereal piece to create a histogram of the sample (see fig. 1.3). Children seemed to enjoy this activity because they could eat the cereal. This task came from an activity in the district's prekindergarten curriculum that covered the Common Core standard K.MD.B.3: Classify objects into given categories; count the numbers of objects in each category and sort the categories by count. But after doing this activity for multiple years, Jones became dissatisfied with it. She did not like the way the activity focused only on individual counting and sorting, nor did she think any of her children cared about the number of different colors in a handful of cereal. The activity did not allow opportunity to collaborate or come together in community. So Jones abandoned this activity in favor of charting and counting tasks that organically came out of her class discussions. In this way, her children could see that mathematics was a community endeavor as they learned to count, classify, and organize the data they generated.

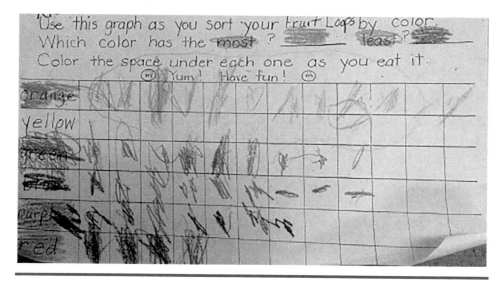

Fig 1.3. The abandoned sorting, counting, and coloring activity involving orange, yellow, green, blue, purple, and red cereal pieces

Second, in Jones's classroom, children's curiosity drives the lesson. Jones constantly takes up and connects children's ideas, utterances, and observations to help children feel ownership in whatever tasks they are doing. This approach leads to collaborative and engaging mathematical discussions that do not dismiss children's mathematical thinking but rather elicit and extend children's ideas, no matter what these may be. For instance, Jones knew that her children loved *The Foot Book* (Seuss 1968) and wanted to create an activity involving measuring the children's feet. Prior to the activity described in the vignette, Jones had children classify their own shoes as either having laces or not having laces. Each child was given a laminated cutout of shoes with laces or without laces; and one at a time, the children placed their "shoes" on a two-column chart (see fig. 1.4). Collectively, the class then counted the number of children in the class who had shoes with laces and the number of children in the class who had shoes without laces. This activity still covers CCSSM K.MD.B.3 as did the activity with the colored cereal, but it also allows children to stand up, place a shoe on a chart, count the number of shoes, and compare which side of the chart has more shoes and which side of the chart has fewer. This activity starts with discrete data—laces vs. no laces—and introduces children to how they can generate data themselves.

Fig. 1.4. Laces vs. no laces laminated "shoes" for children to select

However, Jones still felt this activity was too procedural and did not actively engage children in play as they explored mathematics, a crucial element in prekindergarten teaching (Parks 2015). So when a child suggested tracing feet on the butcher paper, and another child added the suggestion of painting feet, then stepping on butcher paper, Jones took up these ideas and let them drive the lesson. Jones focused the conversation on creating a visual representation of the classroom community but still allowed the children to dictate how they wanted to create and represent the data themselves.

Third, in Jones's classroom, the children worked with data and created mathematical representations meaningful to them. In comparison with the colored cereal (see fig. 1.3) or the Laces vs. No Laces (see fig. 1.4) activities, the foot color circle graph was child-generated, communal, and came from children's ideas.

Fourth, Jones practices responsive teaching by readjusting her own goals for the lesson and being open-ended about where children take a mathematical activity. Jones listened to her children, which led to them representing their data in a circle. Jones and Chao were not sure this approach would work—they thought it would be difficult for the children to create the circle graph—but Jones heard the children's ideas of creating a circular representation and made their ideas happen.

Jones's confidence in the children, as well as her supervision, helped ensure that this representation actually worked to represent the data the children generated.

Fifth, Jones not only fostered a community of mathematics inside her classroom but also connected to the outside community knowledge that children brought with them from home, families, and experiences outside of school. Jones's teaching makes strong connections with her community; parents regularly help out in her classroom, jumping into mathematical tasks and being playful with the children. This connection bridges her children's school experience with family life. Jones reaches out in particular to children who might feel shy or isolated, such as her emerging bilingual children. Additionally, the classroom community atmosphere is constantly negotiated by children, who made *The Foot Book* (Seuss 1968) part of the community landscape by continually requesting it for reading time.

The Evolution of Children's Reasoning on Data and Measurement

Over the years, Jones has embraced different ways to think about data, measurement, and graphing within her prekindergarten classroom. She uses the ideas from the Access and Equity Principle to guide her analysis of how to structure an activity and whether it allows all of her children to engage in mathematical thinking. Here we detail the evolution of the activities that Jones used, rewrote, abandoned, and continues to work on in order to build a level of access and equity into her prekindergarteners' learning of statistical reasoning. Jones wants her children to count, categorize, and sort data into visual representation, such as charts, tables, and graphs, in order to document and analyze mathematical concepts from their everyday life.

First, we have already mentioned how the colored cereal activity (see fig. 1.3) was a classroom staple for many years, mainly because it seemed to be a fun, age-appropriate activity that came directly from the district's model prekindergarten curriculum. However, upon reflection, Jones thought it was too individualistic and inauthentic, because children had little ownership over the data. So this year, Jones decided not to do that activity.

Second, Jones implemented a different activity when reading another Dr. Seuss book, *Green Eggs and Ham* (Seuss 1960). After Jones read the book to the children, they voted on whether they "liked" or "didn't like" green eggs and ham. Jones took a photograph of each child and place it onto a laminated cutout of a green sunny-side-up egg. Then, each child placed his or her green egg on either the "like" side or the "don't like" side of a butcher paper chart. Jones liked how children made observations about which side had more eggs and which side had fewer, helping her see that her children were capable of interpreting data presented in charts. She also liked how children actively placed their cut-out "eggs" onto the graph, showing how engaged children were when physically interacting with the chart. This activity also introduced her children to creating a two-column chart. While Jones noted that children enjoyed this Green Eggs and Ham activity, she felt that voting on "liking" or "not liking" green eggs and ham only introduced the power of using and understanding data. Jones hopes both to expand upon these ideas by using data that are meaningful to children and to engage her children in more generative discussions about representing data.

Third, when discussing an upcoming family night, the children started a conversation about what kind of thank-you gift they should give to each family who attends. In the discussion, children mentioned three ideas of ways to show their gratitude (a word they were learning that day): a thank-you note, a thank-you picture, and thank-you food. Jones built upon this idea and created a three-column chart to organize children's votes. First, she clarified exactly what each category meant by asking children to elaborate on the gifts. The thank-you note would be a card that each child would sign and give to his or her family. The thank-you picture would be a photograph of the child with a short thank-you message written on the back of it. Jones reminded the children that food would already be available at family night—so what did they imagine the thank-you food would be like? One child suggested giving each family a bag of thank-you chips. Other children agreed with this idea. So on the chart, Jones filled in the last column as thank-you chips. Then Jones went through each column and asked children to raise their hand based on which thank-you gift they wanted to give. For each child, she wrote down a tally mark on the chart.

After Jones recorded all the tally marks and counted up the totals, a boy named Brian (a pseudonym) raised his hand and said, "It's not fair. Most people chose all three choices." Jones took up this comment on fairness and asked every child who voted on all three choices to stand up. Only three children stood up. Jones counted, "1, 2, 3. OK, so how many people said all three?" The children responded in unison, "3." Jones asked, "So did most people choose all three?" Brian responded, "A lot of people didn't choose all three. They chose one or two."

Jones asked the class how they could make the voting more fair. Brian then asked, "How many people voted just for one?" Jones responded by asking all the children who voted on just one choice to stand up and move to a corner of the rug. Eight children stood up and moved to the corner of the rug. Jones then asked the children who voted for all three choices to move to the opposite corner of the rug. She then had the children count, together, the number of children in each of the three groups: three children voted for three choices, five children voted for two choices, and eight children voted for just one choice. Jones asked if the voting was fair if five children voted for two choices and three children voted for all three choices. The class came to a consensus that a fair vote meant that each child voted for just one choice. In taking up Brian's comment that the voting was not fair, Jones orchestrated a discussion focused, not on the data, but on how the data were generated and whether these data represented the whole class. Jones focused the conversation around Brian's idea of "it's not fair" and how to ensure that the voting would be fair next time. As the conversation ended, the children decided that the next day, in order to find a clear winner, each child would vote for only one thank-you gift.

Another activity Jones mathematizes in her classroom is something she calls the body parts song. Jones's children love singing the classic song "Heads, Shoulders, Knees, and Toes" and adding their own parts to the song, so it is not just about heads, shoulders, knees, and toes but can incorporate elbows, chins, bellies, shins, ears, whatever the child wants. Jones started a discussion about whether the class should create their own class song as a version of the body parts song. First, she took suggestions from the children about which body parts to include in the song. The discussion was lively as the children laughed at almost every body part, showcasing how Jones tried to keep every activity and discussion playful. Then Jones created a five-column table. In the first column, she wrote every body part mentioned. The successive columns represented the order of the body part in the song. Jones went through each column, having children vote about which body part they wanted to sing about. Jones reminded the children about the idea of fairness that Brian had brought up when they voted on the thank-you gifts. Jones led a discussion about how the class would make sure everyone voted for only one body part. The children decided that, to make sure everyone voted only once, they would all move to different parts of the rug to represent their vote. For instance, to vote for "hair," a child would go to one corner of the rug; to vote for "cheeks," a child would go to another corner; to vote for "shins," a child would go to the table. This method of moving to a different part of the room ensured that each child would vote for only one choice. After Jones ran through four iterations of voting for the four body parts in the song, the class counted up the number of votes for each body part. Jones asked the children which body part in each column had the most votes, circling that particular part of the table. Through this voting and visual data representation, all children created and voted on their new class body parts song. Over the next few weeks, the children sang their new class body parts song, eventually recording it as a video to send to their families. Through this body parts song activity, the children experienced creating, organizing, and voting on which body parts to sing about as a class. In reflection, this was one of the few activities that actually went according to how Jones planned it. But if it had not, she would have followed the children's discussion.

Overall, principles of access and equity play into the evolution of this series of activities. Every week, Jones would try to think of another way to incorporate statistical reasoning into a classroom activity. Jones and Chao would chat briefly, and Jones would try the activity with her children. These activities are about more than boys' vs. girls' feet or a foot color pie chart; they are about the entire process that helps children develop their reasoning over time.

Through these activities, Jones's prekindergarteners engaged in mathematical thinking that went above the content standards for their grade. For instance, these lessons connect with CCSS.1.MD.C.4: Organize, represent, and interpret data with up to three categories; ask and answer questions about the total number of data points, how many in each category, and how many more or less are in one category than in another; and CCSS.K.MD.A.2: Directly compare two objects with a measurable attribute in common, to see which object has "more of"/"less of" the attribute, and describe the difference. For example, directly compare the heights of two children and describe one child as taller/shorter.

Challenges

Teaching prekindergarteners about data and measurement using an access and equity perspective has challenges. For instance, even though Jones wanted children to feel ownership of their data, she sometimes had to interfere with data generation so that the data would be simple enough for children to interpret. In the body parts song activity, for example, Jones casually asked assistants and parents in the room to also vote, in order to ensure one body part would have the "most" votes and to avoid ties.

Additionally, the children often took the discussion in different directions than Jones had planned. In the discussion about thank-you gifts, for example, Brian moved the conversation from deciding on a gift to a conversation about fairness in voting and whether it was fair for children to vote for more than one thank-you gift. Jones orchestrated this conversation to focus on how they could vote so that each child voted only once, leading children to come up with a technique of physically moving to a different part of the rug to vote.

Reflecting and Taking Action

Through this journey, Jones felt that her children engaged much more with mathematics, particularly her children from households that did not have English as their primary language or who started the school year shy and reticent about interacting with peers. A big turning point, in terms of children's empowerment through mathematics, was the body parts song, in which children collectively crafted a song to share with their families. This sense of ownership of data and their representations led to children's confidence to later build their own circle graph when measuring the different feet colors in the class.

Adapting These Activities

Jones used the principles of access and equity so that data, the representation of data, and the creation of the data became meaningful, playful, and fun for all her children. We invite you to adapt these materials for your own classroom so that your children will feel ownership of their own data. While Dr. Seuss's *The Foot Book* (Seuss 1968) played an important part of this classroom's shared knowledge, we invite you to use books and knowledge meaningful to your own children's interest to facilitate playfulness in measurement and data. We end with some reflection questions to help you and the teachers you work with build equitable and accessible measurement and data activities.

Reflection Questions

1. What are meaningful topics or ideas your children can take ownership of and organize in terms of data representation? How can you create spaces for children to share or take ownership of these topics or ideas?

2. How can you allow for children to create and organize their own representations of data, emphasizing the process of creating and analyzing the world around them numerically, rather than creating a predetermined graph? How can you allow for the representation to belong to the children rather than having it be your own?

3. How can you evolve an activity you do in your classroom to focus specifically on your children's agency, equity, and access?

4. How does this activity incorporate elements of children's play, community, and voice?

References

Aguirre, Julia M., Karen Mayfield-Ingram, and Danny Bernard Martin. *The Impact of Identity in K–8 Mathematics: Rethinking Equity-Based Practices.* Reston, Va.: National Council of Teachers of Mathematics, 2013.

Gutiérrez, Rochelle. "A 'Gap-Gazing' Fetish in Mathematics Education? Problematizing Research on the Achievement Gap." *Journal for Research in Mathematics Education* 39, no. 4 (2008): 357–64.

Gutstein, Eric. "'And That's Just How It Starts': Teaching Mathematics and Developing Student Agency." *The Teachers College Record* 109, no. 2 (2007): 420–48.

National Council of Teachers of Mathematics (NCTM). *Principles to Actions: Ensuring Mathematical Success for All.* Reston, Va.: NCTM, 2014.

Parks, Amy Noelle. *Exploring Mathematics through Play in the Early Childhood Classroom.* New York: Teachers College Press, 2015.

Seuss, Dr. *Green Eggs and Ham.* New York: Beginner Books, 1960.

———. *The Foot Book*. New York: Random House Children's Books, 1968.

Turner, Erin E., Mary Q. Foote, Kathleen Jablon Stoehr, Amy Roth McDuffie, Julia Maria Aguirre, Tonya Gau Bartell, and Corey Drake. "Learning to Leverage Children's Multiple Mathematical Knowledge Bases in Mathematics Instruction." *Journal of Urban Mathematics Education* 9, no. 1 (2016): 48–78. http://ed-osprey.gsu.edu/ojs/index.php/JUME/article/view/279

CHAPTER 2

"Tengo toda la receta acá"

Developing Mathematical Agency in Young Emergent Bilinguals

Anne Karabon, *University of Nebraska–Omaha*

Giselle Martinez Negrette, *University of Wisconsin–Madison*

Michelle Smith, *Madison (Wisconsin) Metropolitan School District*

Anita A. Wager, *Vanderbilt University*

It is late spring in Maestra Michelle's four-year-old prekindergarten (4K) emergent bilingual class. The room is set up to support learning through play and exploration; and as is common in early childhood classrooms, a variety of learning areas dominate the room, including a block area, dramatic play, library, water/sensory table, and art area. Maestra Michelle (Maestra M) and the children have recently completed several activities and discussions about seeds, planting, cooking, and food. Following these activities, she added items to support this theme throughout the learning areas in her classroom. The dramatic play area, which usually resembles a household kitchen, is intentionally set up to support interactions focused on baking, including example recipes, measuring cups and spoons of varying sizes, clipboards, and writing utensils.

The writing of this chapter was supported in part by a grant from the National Science Foundation (1019431). The opinions expressed in this chapter do not necessarily reflect the position, policy, or endorsement of the National Science Foundation.

Maestra M is in the dramatic play area with Tomás and Marta. Araceli comes over to her and says, "Tengo toda la receta acá" (*I have the whole recipe here*). Araceli reads her frozen chocolate cake recipe. As she says each ingredient and the amount, Maestra M writes it on the dry-erase chalkboard for other students to see so they too can name the quantity and unit of measurement.

Maestra M: Sería algo congelado, OK, una copa de hielo. ¿Qué más? (*It would be something frozen, OK, one cup of ice. What else?*) [Note: The speaker said *copa*, but *taza* is more accurate in this context. Both words mean "cup."]

Araceli: Dos copas de harina, ha-ri-na. (*Two cups of flour, fl-o-ur.*)

Maestra M: ¿Dos copas de qué? (*Two cups of what?*)

Araceli: Harina. (*Flour.*)

Maestra M: Hari-, exacto, empieza con esas letras, ¡qué lista! Dos copas de ha-ri-na. (*Flo-, exactly, it starts with those letters, how smart! Two cups of fl-o-ur.*)

After a brief interruption from Raphael to ask about a book he is reading, Araceli continues to read her recipe. Tomás sits quietly as Marta continues to work on writing her name on a piece of paper.

Marta: [*shows Maestra M her paper*] ¿Maestra?

Maestra M: ¡A! [*returns to the board and asks Araceli*] ¿Tres copas de azúcar? (A! Three cups of sugar?)

Marta: Sí. (*Yes.*)

Maestra M: Araceli, tienes razón, empieza azúcar con la "A." (*Araceli, you're right, sugar [azúcar] starts with "S" [A].*)

Maestra M: Tres, ooh, sería dulce con tres copas de azúcar. (*Three, ooh, it would be sweet with three cups of sugar.*)

Maestra M: Tres copas de azúcar. ¿Qué más? (*Three cups of sugar. What else?*)

Araceli: Tres copas de chocolate. (*Three cups of chocolate.*)

Maestra M: Ooohh, cho-co-la-te, bate, bate, chocolate, oh son ingredientes. (*Ooohh, cho-co-la-te beat, beat, chocolate, oh they're ingredients.*)

Tomás: Todo chocolate, mi hermana usa eso todo chocolate. (*All chocolate, my sister uses all chocolate.*)

Maestra M: ¿Dos huevos? (*Two eggs?*)

Araceli:	Sí. (*Yes.*)
Maestra M:	Dos huevos. ¿Qué más necesitamos para hacer un pastel de chocolate? (*Two eggs. What else do we need to make a chocolate cake?*)
Tomás:	Huevos. (*Eggs.*)
Maestra M:	Ya hemos dicho dos huevos. ¿Mantequilla? (*We have already said two eggs. Butter?*)
Araceli:	No. (*No.*)
Maestra M:	¿No? (*No?*)
Araceli:	Manzanas. (*Apples.*)
Maestra M:	Pastel de chocolate con manzanas. ¿Cuántas manzanas? (*Chocolate cake with apples. How many apples?*)
Araceli:	Trece. (*Thirteen.*)
Maestra M:	¿Trece? Oh, hay mucho trabajo, pelarlas, cortarlas, quitarles las semillas. OK, trece manzanas. (*Thirteen? Oh, that's a lot of work, peeling, cutting and taking out the seeds. OK, thirteen apples.*)
Tomás:	Eso es mucho. Fresas. (*That's a lot. Strawberries.*)
Maestra M:	Debes hacer pastel de tomate. ¡Te encantan tomates tanto! (*You should make a tomato cake. You love tomatoes!*)

The next day, Tomás writes recipes by drawing pictures and writing numbers next to each ingredient.

Making a Commitment to Access and Equity

The interaction in the vignette described above took only two and half minutes, yet this spontaneous response to what children were doing opened up mathematics learning opportunities for many children in the class that day and in the weeks that followed. Also evident were ways the teacher supported literacy development in the children's native language (see chapters 3 and 4). The loss of learning experiences that emphasize discovery, exploration, and open-ended discussion is disproportionally devastating for children from marginalized communities (Adair 2014). This, coupled with the negative imagery of Latina/o children and families prevalent in media, makes it imperative that we provide evidence of culturally and developmentally responsive mathematics teaching practices that support young emergent bilinguals with opportunities to engage in rich mathematics. Maestra M's prekindergarten classroom does just that and more as she actively embodies principles of pedagogical equity, critical thinking, and ownership in learning. The four- and five-year-old emergent bilinguals in her room have multiple opportunities to learn mathematics throughout the day as she endeavors to "slip math in" to activities from problem solving at breakfast to finding patterns in the clothes they wear. In this chapter, we explore how Maestra M's teaching practices communicate a powerful message of agency in mathematics to young children that positively affects their learning process and identity as Spanish-speaking mathematicians. Looking at these teaching practices can provide insight into how mathematical knowledge can be part of the daily activities of children at a very young age and how teachers can actively guide students to take ownership of their learning. Further, Maestra M demonstrates ways to overcome the obstacles to equitable classrooms that are raised in *Principles to Actions: Ensuring Mathematical Success for All* (NCTM 2014) by providing quality instruction, differentiating opportunities to learn, and holding high expectations (see chapter 1).

Maestra Michelle

In a partnership with the local school district, researchers from the University of Wisconsin–Madison, supported by funding from the National Science Foundation, facilitated and studied a professional development program (the 4KPD Project) to support teachers of four-year-old kindergarten to reconceptualize their pedagogical practices of early mathematics. (The local district offers public prekindergarten to four-year-old children. This half-day program is referred to as 4K.) Teachers worked together to construct new understandings of what culturally and developmentally responsive number and counting looked like in their classrooms. Through discussions, written reflections, and creating action research projects based on children's funds of knowledge (González, Moll, and Amanti 2005), teachers critically thought about embedded mathematics, how to encourage mathematics talk, and ways to highlight mathematics in play. The research aspect of the program involved interviews, audio recorded professional development sessions (PD seminar), and classroom observations.

We first met Maestra M (Michelle Smith, one of the authors of this chapter) in 2011 when she enrolled in the professional development program facilitated by two of this chapter's authors, Anita Wager and Anne Karabon. She had accepted a new position as a 4K teacher with the rollout of the district's new public prekindergarten program. Maestra M, a native English speaker, had previously taught middle school Spanish and a bilingual prekindergarten summer class. Her primary goal was to honor young children's native language by focusing on concepts, such as numeral recognition and counting, in Spanish. Specifically, she hoped the professional development program would help her gain confidence and new ideas about how to better instruct number concepts to emergent bilinguals. After spending two years with a group of fellow 4K teachers, Maestra M completed the professional development program with increased confidence in teaching mathematics, an understanding of how to connect children's mathematical experiences outside of school, and a deeper sense of community with colleagues.

Two years after the conclusion of the project, we started an extension research study to video record mathematics learning opportunities in 4K classrooms (see chapter 9). Because of Maestra M's role as a bilingual teacher, she was selected to participate in this additional research component. Giselle Martinez Negrette, a Spanish-speaking research team member (and another of this chapter's authors), directed a professional videographer to record Maestra M's morning 4K class on eight different occasions, resulting in approximately twenty-four hours of video.

The bilingual 4K classroom in this study, which we will call Room 3, is located at Wayside Elementary. In Room 3, all students except one speak Spanish as their first language, and the majority are of Mexican descent. Children in 4K at Wayside Elementary learn in a developmental bilingual education program format. Teachers provide 90 percent of all instruction (including mathematics) in the children's first language on a temporary basis before they are transitioned to instruction exclusively in English. Using this program model, Maestra M draws on the language (and other) resources that children bring (funds of knowledge) to provide a strong linguistic and academic foundation. The developmental bilingual education program model is only followed in this setting for the 4K academic year, and once children advance to kindergarten and elementary school years, they may encounter different language models. Here we report on aspects of the learning environment that positively affect the first academic experiences of these prekindergarten children.

The vignette that opened this chapter was not a one-time event but an exemplar of the ways in which Maestra M provides access to a high-quality curriculum, engages children in challenging tasks and discourse, leverages children's culture, and supports agency—each of which is an indicator of mathematics teaching that supports access and equity (NCTM 2014, p. 59).

Leveraging Children's Culture

Maestra M's commitment to equity and access is evident in the opening vignette as she provides children with opportunities to learn important mathematics through modeling and supports children's agency and identities as Latina/o and Spanish-speaking mathematicians. She believes that all children enter schooling with knowledge, skills, interests, and expertise that they have learned by observing and participating in everyday experiences. She aims to know where children come from and use what they bring as a base to build learning experiences (Planas and Civil 2013; Wager 2012; also see chapters 7 and 10).

Maestra M is deeply committed to providing equitable access to mathematics (and other) learning to the emergent bilinguals in her classroom. Her philosophy is that the "children are the knowledgeable ones and that she is just facilitating." This is evident in the opening vignette when children are allowed to choose their own ingredients, write a recipe their own way, and have it shared their own way. Maestra M affirms any ideas they have (e.g., three cups of sugar and thirteen apples) with authentic responses and without empty praise. Maestra M's inflection and use of interjections (e.g., "Ooh!"; "No?!"; "Oh! That's a lot of work . . . ") demonstrate her active participation in the play scenario. Her response honors contributions to writing the recipe, knowing that the goal is to encourage children's use of numerals, not ensuring accuracy for baking success.

Classrooms that support equitable mathematics leverage the home and community practices children bring, including cultural and linguistic resources (Turner et al. 2012; Wager 2012). Maestra M does this by honoring children's language, learning from their cultural practices, and welcoming families into the classroom. She recognizes that knowledge can show up in many different ways, that it does not always mirror the formalized practices of schooling (Heath 1983). For instance, children may learn different counting strategies in their homes and use those in the classroom, such as how they count on their fingers. There are many approaches to using fingers for counting, including starting with the thumb or index or pinkie finger, counting each knuckle, or also counting toes (Zaslavsky 1979). Maestra M admits that understanding unique counting practices may not always be obvious when first observed by a teacher. However, by posing open-ended questions with families she has been able to find out that many of her young students sit with older siblings at night as they do homework and are replicating these practices in play.

Providing Access to a High-Quality Mathematics Curriculum

Mathematics curriculum in prekindergarten is often quite different from that found in kindergarten and beyond. Although there are some mathematics curricula explicitly for early childhood, such as Building Blocks for Math (Clements and Sarama 2003), many prekindergarten classrooms use an integrated curriculum that focuses on play as the primary vehicle for learning. In Maestra M's district, all 4K classrooms are provided with Creative Curriculum (Copley, Jones, and Dighe 2010), which is a research-based guide designed to support high-quality, play-based programs that are developmentally appropriate. Maestra M uses Creative Curriculum as a way to frame her philosophy and provide inspiration but often develops her own curricular activities that directly respond to the needs and interests of the children in her classroom and incorporates the elements we see as necessary to provide a culturally and developmentally responsive play-based curriculum. Those elements of high-quality early childhood mathematics curriculum include

(1) *brief* intentional mathematics instruction that, over the course of the year, covers mathematics topics appropriate for early childhood and responds to children's understanding and interests; (2) carefully seeded interest areas that encourage multiple opportunities to engage with mathematics tools, manipulatives, vocabulary, and ideas; and (3) observing, recognizing, and responding to mathematics that emerges through play. (Wager 2013, p. 178)

In the vignette, we see evidence of Maestra M observing, recognizing, and responding to the mathematics that emerged in play; but for that to happen, Maestra M had to organize her classroom in the days and weeks prior to and following the vignette to plan for intentional instruction and to seed the environment with materials that encouraged the children's mathematical thinking. She purposefully provided prior experience with similar materials across different learning areas, not just in dramatic play. The children had access to the same measuring cups in the sensory table (a shallow, child-sized table filled with various materials that promote tactile discovery) to measure beans and water. By putting out materials that support mathematical thinking (measuring cups, teaspoons, tablespoons, visuals on the walls that show a picture representation and sizes of recipes), the children were supported to engage in mathematics in multiple ways. The combination of these purposeful, seeded, and responding to play moves on the teacher's part provided a high-quality, engaging "curriculum" (National Research Council 2009).

Engaging Children with Challenging Tasks, Discourse, and Open-Ended Problem Solving

Maestra M has seen that in similar recipe-writing activities, other teachers might provide children with a worksheet that includes items for children to check off. Instead, Maestra M provides children with a blank piece of paper for them to make their own choices based on their interests, level of engagement, and where they are mathematically. For example, Tomás filled his recipe card with a whole page of pictures and numbers, whereas Araceli "wrote" the recipe using the correct initial letters for the ingredients. In providing the blank sheet, Maestra M was asking children to write but left open how and what they wrote and honored whatever was on the paper. Tomás was able to make this activity his own because Maestra M did not put barriers on the ways children might approach the work. The open activities in the classroom allow for children to access the learning where they are and also see more sophisticated approaches. The spontaneous recipe-writing activity was taken up the next day, with Tomás and Araceli positioned as experts.

One of the beauties of a play-based classroom is that children are not grouped for learning activities. So even though Tomás might be at one place academically and Araceli at another, they are still playing and learning together because Maestra M provides opportunities that are open and accessible to all. Maestra M provides differentiated instruction, individualized scaffolding, and a variety of supports for all students, regardless of background characteristics. She is keen to deliver equitable (not equal) tasks and discourse to achieve meaningful outcomes (Gutiérrez 2013).

In many prekindergarten classrooms, mathematics in play is not always evident to teachers, for a variety of reasons (see Wager and Parks 2014). Yet, we argue there were several rich, embedded mathematics learning opportunities in the vignette. It may appear at first glance that this activity is primarily a literacy activity. However, Maestra M incorporates mathematics into various aspects of the play. For instance, when Araceli says that her recipe includes thirteen apples, Maestra M extends this idea by describing the amount in the set thirteen rather than on the name of the number. Focusing on the meaning of quantity, she adds that prepping that many apples would require a significant amount of time.

Advancing Access and Equity

In Room 3, Maestra M strives to provide a context conducive to the production of personal and social identities of her students. She supports them to be confident by furthering their development of mathematical concepts with critical thinking and problem-solving skills. Maestra M understands that she is responsible for facilitating learning and also acknowledges that children participate in making sense of content and concepts. As they do so, they are actively co-constructing the idea that they are capable and confident mathematics learners by accepting, rejecting, and negotiating the identities being offered (Urrieta 2007). In an interview at the close of the PD program, Maestra M reflects,

> It's good for kids to say, "I know with my math," but part of it is also the encouraging critical thinking and problem solving; letting them figure it out. I'm not going to answer right away. I tell them: "you tell me what you think" or "you can ask a friend" [because it promotes language development]. I can't give them everything. I bring the scaffolding. I meet them where they are and then see where they will go. (Interview, May 2015)

In early childhood classrooms, children of immigrants, in poverty, and/or emergent bilinguals tend to have less exposure to the design of projects, exploration, and experimentation (Adair 2014). They are most likely to find themselves in classrooms that are standards-driven and with less access to rich learning activities. However, when provided the educative opportunity to collaborate in open-ended discussions, young emergent bilinguals are able to use their language as a vehicle for critical thinking and problem solving. Similarly, in regard to mathematics, when teachers challenge traditional pedagogical practices that focus more on procedural and direct learning, children have access to high-quality and rigorous learning experiences (NCTM 2014).

By keeping in mind that children bring their previous experiences and understandings of the world with them to school, teachers provide the opportunity to cultivate diversity as a resource when organizing mathematical learning experiences and planning a curriculum that draws on children's backgrounds. This means teachers attend to access and equitable mathematics practices for all students regardless of race, ethnicity, ability, gender, wealth, and native language. To achieve equity, we need to believe that mathematics ability is of opportunity, experiences, and effort; children should receive differentiated supports (e.g., time and instruction); children demonstrate their mathematical understandings in various ways; and partnering with families and communities is powerful (NCTM 2014, pp. 63–64). (See also chapters 6 and 7.)

Maestra M possesses these dispositions and, through multiple teaching and learning strategies, delivers high-quality mathematics instruction for young emergent bilingual children. In returning to the vignette that opened this chapter, we see evidence of the ways she supports children's mathematics learning by the way she attends to their mathematical thinking (Carpenter et al. 2014); develops their literacy in Spanish and treats their home language as a resource (Moschkovich 2013); and connects to their interests in popular culture, which Hedges (2011) describes as a particular kind of fund of knowledge for young children. When Maestra M says "Ooohh, cho-co-la-te, bate, bate, chocolate, oh son ingredientes," she is referring to a song from *Dora the Explorer* (a popular children's cartoon show in which the main character, Dora, speaks both English and Spanish). She knows the children in her class watch the program and uses this as an opportunity to promote literacy and connect to something fun that interests them.

Culturally Responsive Curriculum

Maestra M uses a play-based curriculum that includes a plethora of visual materials and props to support learning activities. Pedagogically, she believes that mathematics is embedded in all aspects of the classroom. She uses routine times, individual interactions, and play to model problem-solving skills. During meals, she chooses a student to count the number of children in class and the number of utensils they need for that day. She draws on children's attention to patterns in their clothes and assists them in creating their own patterns when they are drawing.

Maestra M works purposefully to set up her classroom so that children see their culture reflected in the materials they use and the practices they engage with. One way she does this is by noticing, listening, and learning about what students experience outside the classroom. She then incorporates those elements into learning experiences during play. For example, in the dramatic play area, she adds ethnic toy food and tablecloths resembling those often found in Mexican restaurants. For some, this may appear as a touristic approach to incorporating artifacts; however, when children engage in this area, they use imaginative play to turn blocks into tortilla warmers for their food. Maestra M encourages them to write their own recipes or to put prices on food that they serve at their classroom restaurant. Children demonstrate their cultural understandings and practices with the materials that Maestra M provides.

Another way Maestra M helps children see their culture in the classroom is by learning the songs and rhymes that the children know. As is common in early childhood classrooms, Maestra M uses counting books to support the learning of counting. She introduces the books by reading them in Spanish for a full week, then reading them in English. Maestra M makes sure to use the Spanish version of common early childhood counting books such as *Cinco monitos brincando en la cama*, *Diez patitos de goma*, *Diez pequeñas mariquitas*, *Diez perritos*, and *Cuenta ratones*. She also uses books to support children's understanding of measurement (*¿Por qué medimos?*), addition (*Sumemos con el dominó*), and position vocabulary (*Arriba, abajo y alrededor* and *¿Dónde está el pingüino Pips?*). Maestra M invites children to say the counting words aloud with her, encourages the use of fingers to count, and continually asks them questions such as "How many do we have left?" or "How many do we have now?" to support their understanding of one-to-one correspondence and cardinality (National Research Council 2009).

When Maestra M cannot find the books in Spanish, she makes them herself. The popular children's book *Diez en la cama* (Ten in the Bed) was only available in a mini-book version, so Maestra M used small stuffed animals and took photos to make her own Spanish version of the book (see figs. 2.1 and 2.2).

Photo by Michelle Smith

Fig. 2.1. Maestra M's "Ten in the Bed"

Fig. 2.2. Maestra M's "Seven in the Bed"

The lack of resources in Spanish does not deter Maestra M from working on providing significant mathematical experiences for her students. On the contrary, as the examples above show, she has learned how to adapt her mathematics curriculum materials, exhibiting a high regard for meeting the Access and Equity Principle. It is also noticeable how Maestra M strives to connect the linguistic and cultural assets students bring to the classroom to the lessons and activities that she designs and implements (see chapter 10). In the following description of her efforts on behalf of her students, Maestra M shows how she strives to apply the Access and Equity Principle in her classroom.

> There's a good song in the district's math curriculum for counting backwards from fifteen to the tune of "Happy Birthday." Counting backwards from fifteen is hard because they don't have the sight recognition of those big numbers plus the going backwards bit too. But when we do it in Spanish, it doesn't have the same resonance because they only kinda sorta know the English happy birthday tune. The Spanish happy birthday song [that we normally sing], "Las Mañanitas," doesn't have the same rhythm. So I try to find songs that will translate well, like "Five Green and Speckled Frogs." (PD seminar, September 2011)

Language as a Tool

Most of the children in Maestra M's classroom speak Spanish in their homes. In Room 3, children are supported to socially construct meaning using the Spanish language as the vehicle of communication. Maestra M encourages *translanguaging.* This term, popularized by García (2009) in the United States and Baker (2011) in the United Kingdom, refers to an additive approach to bilingualism in which all students' language practices are honored and used in the complex discursive practices of the classroom space. The process of translanguaging sustains old language practices while allowing new communication patterns to be developed.

In Maestra M's classroom, children always have a choice about what language they speak. In terms of learning mathematics, particularly counting, that means they can use English, Spanish, or a mix of the two for counting words. Although both languages are respected, Spanish is the dominant language used in Room 3. In a whole-group lesson, Maestra M takes the lead of Iker, a predominantly Spanish-speaking student.

> Maestra M: Iker quiere contar algunos en inglés, OK. Vamos a empezar otra
>   vez para que todos puedan escucharlo, ¿OK? (*Iker wants to count*
>   *some in English, OK. We are going to start again, so that everyone*
>   *can hear it OK?*) [*in English:*] 1, 2, 3, 4, 5, 6, 7, 8, 9, 10, 11, 12, 13,
>   14, 15, 16, 17, 18, 19, 20, 21, 22, 23, 24, 25 . . .
>
> Students: 26, 27, 28, 29.

(Classroom observation, April 2015)

Collaborative and Differentiated Mathematical Instruction

Maestra M firmly believes in adapting instruction to meet the needs of all students while maintaining high expectations (NCTM 2014). It is important to mention here that for Maestra M, "adapting instruction" does not mean "watering down" the curriculum for her students. On the contrary, it involves an ongoing process of innovation in her practices and the promotion of new ways to use mathematics with the students, as we can see in the opening vignette. In Maestra M's classroom, children self-select open-ended activities and are encouraged to ask questions of one another to solve problems. Although her practices also reflect traditional early childhood approaches to learning, her use of visual materials and props to support the learning activities is remarkable. In addition, her use of embedded and explicit mathematics is prevalent in all aspects of the classroom. Maestra M explains her approach:

> To me, discovery—how to inquire about something and be inquisitive—is so much richer and so much more useful down the line of learning. Be curious and learn through your curiosity. Yes, we will rote count, we will rote count a lot but also the asking, the experimenting. That is key. (Interview, May 2013)

Her role as a teacher is deeply focused on engaging students in activities that promote reasoning and problem solving. With this goal in mind, she "facilitate[s] discourse that moves students toward shared understanding of mathematics" (NCTM 2014, p. 11). Maestra M continually positions her students as autonomous and knowledgeable learners. She is often heard reminding people in Room 3 that the children should try solving problems on their own before asking an adult for assistance.

Assessments That Demonstrate Mathematical Thinking

Maestra M's understanding, design, and implementation of assessments reflect culturally and linguistically responsive approaches that help children show evidence of their mathematical thinking. Before emergent bilinguals begin kindergarten in Maestra M's school district, they complete a screening that includes an in-depth home language survey as well as an in-school assessment. Maestra M recognizes that context matters when conducting assessments in school and that they may not always capture all of a child's skills and abilities.

> Some of these kids do things at home that I don't see at school. And it doesn't mean that they're not ready for schooling. Their skills just might not show up in the way we assess. And that doesn't mean they don't have knowledge in that area. For example, I do not see my student Fabio drawing shapes in class, but his family says that he does at home. Then in the screener, I saw it. And I'm like, "You've got to be kidding me! That's a triangle, that's a circle, that's a square—no way!" So if I can learn from families by asking, "When does he do that? When does he sit down and draw? What is he talking about when he draws? How can I do that so I can see it here?" So if there's something a kid's not able to do in school, we cannot say, "Well, they don't know that." We need to find out what they do at home and try to figure out how to bridge that, that home-to-school discrepancy. (Interview, May 2013)

Young children may produce content knowledge in different ways in different spaces that may be attributed to the ways in which they are being asked to produce and demonstrate their knowledge (Heath 1983; Souto-Manning 2013). Some teachers perceive this cultural disconnect to mean that children from minority and/or low resource homes are "behind." In order to counter this deficit perspective and thinking, Maestra M continues to examine informal ways that young children make sense of the world and how to use observations of play as a way to assess their skills and abilities.

School and Community Partnerships

Families know that they are welcome in Maestra M's classroom. Although many of the families are working during school hours, those who are able often spend time in the classroom after drop-off or before pick-up times. Family members read stories or participate in play. Parents are often included in counting activities during birthday celebrations, and they also share their knowledge about mathematical practices when they join their children during breakfast time. They help children count breakfast items and ask them questions about the meal. Maestra M is particularly interested in creating bridges between the families and the school community (see chapters 6 and 7).

> Parents come in and sometimes read books and sing songs. It's such a connection because the kids would be like, oh, I know that song, my mom sings that at home! When I invite parents to come in, we are able to talk and I tend to find out information about their daily home experiences and family practices. (Interview, May 2015)

Maestra M is aware that children's funds of knowledge, home experiences, and culture play a pivotal role in their understanding of content knowledge. This is why she makes an effort to connect with their families in order to inform her teaching practices. She considers it crucial to understand not only what students do at home but also how they are experiencing mathematical learning at home. In this way, she ensures that the linguistic and cultural resources used in the classroom reflect children's lives, their home practices, and hobbies.

Reflecting and Taking Action

Reflection Questions

1. Think about your own classroom. What are the practices you engage in that support children's agency?

2. Because Maestra M's classroom is play based, she has some flexibility in her curriculum. How might you modify your curriculum to incorporate some of the same strategies Maestra M uses?

3. In taking an assets-based approach to her work with children, Maestra M starts with what they know. What are the mathematical strengths evident in each child in the opening vignette?

Actions for Teachers

Maestra M intentionally creates a space where mathematical learning is not a difficult task but part of children's daily lives. That said, she is always finding ways to challenge herself as an educator. Her educational philosophy is linked to the words of Paulo Freire regarding the nature of education: "Something I want to work on next year is inquiry-based and discovery play. I want them to ask, 'Why does my tower keep falling down?' I want them to try something, try it again, and try to fix it" (Interview, May 2013). Maestra M constantly looks for new things to learn and creative ways to connect and engage in mathematical learning with her students.

Her practices encourage teachers to consider ways in which they might be separating mathematical teaching from the everyday interactions of the children and the reasons behind this. Teachers might also reflect on their own perceptions regarding emergent bilinguals. How do you see emergent bilinguals in your classrooms? Are you leveraging the children's culture to provide access to a high-quality mathematics curriculum through collaborative and differentiated mathematical instruction? What are the positions offered to students through classroom interactions? We consider that Maestra M's practices send a powerful message to her students of agency in mathematics that positively affect their learning process. It is in educational environments like the one presented here, where children and their cultural knowledge and linguistic background are seen as an asset to learning in the classroom. Maestra M's practices fully embody principles of pedagogical equity, critical thinking, and the belief that all children should have access to high-quality education.

Keeping in mind that the "teachers' beliefs influence the decisions that they make about the manner in which they teach mathematics [. . . and] students' beliefs influence their perception of what it means to learn mathematics and their dispositions toward the subject" (NCTM 2014, pp. 10–11), we consider it significant to examine teaching practices, such as the one presented in this chapter, to create useful teaching work. As mentioned above, Maestra M not only takes into consideration the cultural and linguistic diversity of her students, but also makes a commitment to access and equity for all learners. To this end, she leverages children's culture, providing access to a high-quality mathematics curriculum through collaborative and differentiated mathematical instruction. What is more, her assessments take into consideration the diverse ways in which students can demonstrate their mathematical thinking and reveal the importance of students' funds of knowledge in mathematical learning and instruction. Creating this type of environment and designing appropriate activities to connect all these elements is not an easy task. She is constantly faced with institutional arrangements structured around budget restrictions and constraining educational policies and reforms. However, her teaching practices display a commitment to access and equity that goes beyond the circumscription of the physical space of the classroom to create school and community partnerships with families.

References

Adair, Jennifer Keys. "Agency and Expanding Capabilities in Early Grade Classrooms: What It Could Mean for Young Children." *Harvard Educational Review* 84, no. 2 (2014): 217–24.

Baker, Colin. *Foundations of Bilingual Education and Bilingualism.* 5th ed. Clevedon, United Kingdom: Multilingual Matters, 2011.

Carpenter, Thomas. P., Elizabeth Fennema, Megan Loef Franke, Linda Levi, and Susan Empson. *Children's Mathematics: Cognitively Guided Instruction.* Portsmouth, N.H.: Heineman, 2014.

Clements, Douglas, and Julie Sarama. *Building Blocks—SRA Real Math Teacher's Edition, Grade PreK.* Columbus, Ohio: SRA/McGraw-Hill, 2003.

Copley, Juanita, Candy Jones, and Judith Dighe. *The Creative Curriculum for Preschool: Mathematics.* Washington D.C.: Teaching Strategies, 2010.

García, Ofelia. *Bilingual Education in the 21st Century: A Global Perspective.* Malden, Mass.: Basil/Blackwell, 2009.

González, Norma, Luis Moll, and Cathy Amanti. *Funds of Knowledge: Theorizing Practices in Households, Communities, and Classrooms.* Mahwah, N.J.: Lawrence Erlbaum Associates, 2005.

Gutiérrez, Rochelle. "The Sociopolitical Turn in Mathematics Education." *Journal for Research in Mathematics Education* 44, no. 1 (2013): 37–68.

Heath, Shirley Brice. *Ways with Words: Language, Life, and Work in Communities and Classrooms.* Cambridge, United Kingdom: Cambridge University Press, 1983.

Hedges, Helen. "Rethinking Sponge Bob and Ninja Turtles: Popular Culture as Funds of Knowledge for Curriculum Co-construction." *Australasian Journal of Early Childhood* 36, no. 1 (2011): 25–29.

Moschkovich, Judit N. "Principles and Guidelines for Equitable Mathematics Teaching Practices and Materials for English Language Learners." *Journal for Urban Mathematics Education* 6, no. 1 (2013): 45–51.

National Council of Teachers of Mathematics (NCTM). *Principles to Actions: Ensuring Mathematical Success for All.* Reston, Va.: NCTM, 2014.

National Research Council. *Mathematics Learning in Early Childhood: Pathways toward Excellence and Equity.* Washington, D.C.: National Academies Press, 2009.

Planas, Núria, and Marta Civil. "Language-as-Resource and Language-as-Political: Tensions in the Bilingual Mathematics Classroom." *Mathematics Education Research* 25, no. 3 (2013): 361–78.

Souto-Manning, Mariana. *Multicultural Teaching in the Early Childhood Classroom.* New York: Teachers College Press, 2013.

Turner, Erin E., Corey Drake, Amy Roth McDuffie, Julia Aguirre, Tonya Gau Bartell, and Mary Q. Foote. "Promoting Equity in Mathematics Teacher Preparation: A Framework for Advancing Teacher Learning of Children's Multiple Mathematics Knowledge Bases." *Journal of Mathematics Teacher Education* 15, no. 1 (2012): 67–82.

Urrieta, Luis. "Identity Production in Figured Worlds: How Some Mexican Americans become Chicana/o Activist Educators." *The Urban Review* 39, no. 2 (2007): 117–44.

Wager, Anita A. "Incorporating Out-of-School Mathematics: From Cultural Context to Embedded Practice." *Journal of Mathematics Teacher Education* 15, no. 1 (2012): 9–23.

———. "Practices That Support Mathematics Learning in a Play-Based Classroom." In *Reconceptualizing Early Mathematics Learning,* edited by Lynn English and J. Mulligan, pp. 163–81. Dordrecht, The Netherlands: Springer, 2013.

Wager, Anita, and Amy Noelle Parks. "Learning Mathematics through Play." In *SAGE Handbook of Play and Learning in Early Childhood,* edited by Elizabeth Brooker, Mindy Blaise, and Susan Edwards, pp. 216–27. London, United Kingdom: Sage Publications, 2014.

Zaslavsky, Claudia. "It's Okay to Count on Your Fingers." *Teacher* 96, Spring/Summer (1979): 54–56.

Children's Picture Books Referenced

Ada, Alma Flor, F., Isabel Campoy, Ulises Wensell, and Rosa Zubizarreta. *Ten Little Puppies / Diez perritos: Adaptación de una canción infantil tradicional.* New York: Rayo, 2011.

Ayres, Katherine, and Nadine Bernard Westcott. *Arriba, abajo y alrededor.* Somerville, Mass.: Candlewick Press, 2014.

Carle, Eric. *Diez patitos de goma.* New York: Rayo, 2007.

Christelow, Eileen. *Cinco monitos brincando en la dama = Five Little Monkeys Jumping on the Bed.* New York: Clarion Books, 2005.

Gerth, Melanie. *Diez pequeñas mariquitas.* Santa Monica, Calif.: Piggy Toes Press, 2000.

Junakovic, Svjetlan. *¿Dónde está el pingüino Pips?* Buenos Aires: UnaLuna, 2006.

Long, Lynette. *Sumemos con el dominó.* Watertown, Mass.: Charlesbridge, 1997.

Thompson, Kim Mitzo. *Diez en la cama (Ten in the Bed).* Worthington, Ohio: Brighter Child, 2006.

Trumbauer, Lisa. *¿Por qué medimos?* Mankato, Minn.: Yellow Umbrella Press, 2005.

Walsh, Ellen. *Cuenta ratones.* San Diego, Calif.: Harcourt Brace Jovanovich, 1995.

CHAPTER 3

¿Qué observamos aquí? ¿Qué preguntas tienen?

Problem Posing in Ms. Bustillos's Second-Grade Bilingual Classroom

Erin E. Turner, *The University of Arizona*

Lus M. Bustillos, *Tucson (Arizona) Unified School District*

Ms. Bustillos's second-grade emerging bilingual students often talk about their school's newly established school store, where students can exchange tickets, earned for kind actions and positive behaviors, for supplies such as notebooks, pencils, and chapter books. Students are often observed counting their tickets and talking about what they would like to purchase at the store and about how many more tickets they might need. Given students' interest and experiences with the school store, Ms. Bustillos used this context as the basis for a problem-posing discussion.

She started by projecting photos of baskets from the store that held different items for sale. Ms. Bustillos then asked students to share what they noticed: "¿Qué observan? ¿Qué es lo que vemos en la tiendita, que le decimos el 'grabber store'?" (*What do you observe? What do we see in the little store, that we call the "grabber store"?*). Students excitedly listed the various items that they saw for sale (i.e., notebooks, chapter books, pencils, stickers) and discussed their own purchases. Ms. Bustillos then asked students to think about questions, or things that they wondered, based on what they saw in the photos: "¿Qué preguntas tienen de la tiendita? ¿Qué preguntas podemos crear, basado en lo que vemos?" (*What kinds of questions can we come up with, based on what we see?*). As the discussion continued, students generated questions about topics such as the prices of different items, the number of items sold during the school year, how tickets are made, and what happens to tickets once they are used. Ms. Bustillos then asked students if they would like to see the list of prices.

Ms. Bustillos:	Algunos tenían preguntas de cuánto vale cada cosa. Nosotros sí tenemos la lista de los precios. ¿La quieren ver? (*Some of you had questions about how much each item cost. We have the list of prices. Would you like to see it?*)
Students:	¡Sí! (*Yes!*)

Ms. Bustillos projected the list of prices, in tickets, for different items (see fig. 3.1). She then asked students to review the prices and to talk with peers about additional questions they had about the school store. What followed was a lively discussion during which students asked clarifying questions about the list of prices. For instance, one student wondered about the multiple items listed after each number of tickets. (We have used pseudonyms for the students.)

Felipe:	So if we have 150 grabbers [tickets], why do we get a sports ball and a football and a soccer ball and a basketball?
Ms. Bustillos:	Good question. So do you think this means that for 150 grabbers you can get all four balls, or one ball?
Felipe:	Only one?
Ms. Bustillos:	Right, so this means if you have 150 grabbers, you can pick one ball, which could be a football, or a basketball, or a soccer ball.

1 Grabber =	1 item from the white basket (plain #2 pencil, eraser, 1 sticker, bookmark, etc.)
5 Grabbers =	1 item from purple plastic container (design pencil, sticker sheet, mechanical pencil, cool eraser, etc.)
10 Grabbers =	1 item from pink basket (chapter book, box of crayons, plain notebook, toy)
20 Grabbers =	1 item from red basket (markers, pencil box, cool pens, eraser/sharpener duo)
30 Grabbers =	1 item from green basket (books, toys, design notebooks, folders), OR 4 chapter books
150 Grabbers =	1 sports ball (football, soccer ball, basketball)

Fig. 3.1. Ticket prices of items at the school "grabber" store

Other students asked questions about the logistics of the store (i.e., who copied the tickets) that, while interesting, were unlikely to lead to problems students could investigate mathematically. Ms. Bustillos acknowledged students' questions but also invited them to generate mathematical questions, reminding them of a class anchor chart that listed "question starters" in both English and Spanish (see fig. 3.2). This helped students generate a range of mathematical problems that reflected their own experiences and "wonderings" about the school store. For example,

Ramón: If I had 20 grabbers, and then I get 30 grabbers more, what can I buy?

Sara: How many grabbers do I need to get 2 soccer balls?

Anabel: Si tengo 62 grabbers, y agarro cuatro chapter books, ¿cúantos grabbers me quedan? (*If I have 62 grabbers and I get 4 chapter books, how many grabbers do I have left?*)

Josue: How many grabbers do I need to buy one thing from each basket?

Giovanny: If I have 150 grabbers, what can I buy?

Jasmin: If I have 98 grabbers, how many pencils can I buy?

Daniela: Si tengo 30 grabbers y quiero una pelota, ¿cuántos más necesito? (*If I have 30 grabbers and I want a ball, how many more do I need?*)

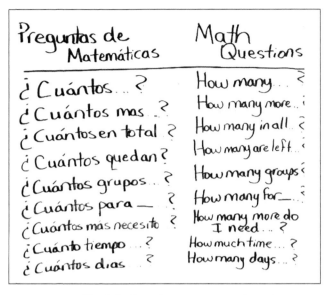

Fig. 3.2. Question starters anchor chart

Ms. Bustillos recorded each question on the whiteboard for students and also asked students to restate and/or translate peers' questions in their own words. For instance, following Anabel's question (Si tengo 62 grabbers, y agarro cuatro chapter books, ¿cúantos grabbers me quedan? [*If I have 62 grabbers and I get 4 chapter books, how many grabbers do I have left?*]), Ms. Bustillos asked, "¿Quién me puede decir lo que dijo Anabel, pero en inglés?" (*Who can tell me what Anabel said, but in English?*). Next, Ms. Bustillos guided students to select several questions to investigate in their small groups. Students decided to start with the problems posed by Anabel, Josue, and Giovanny, and spent the remainder of the class period generating various solutions. With Giovanny's question (If I have 150 grabbers, what can I buy?), Ms. Bustillos reminded students that they should be creative and look for multiple solutions. She explained:

> Pueden ser muy creativos con lo que pueden comprar con los 150 grabbers. Podrían comprar nada más una pelota, pero queremos que encuentren muchas opciones. (*You can be very creative with what you can buy with the 150 grabbers. You could just buy a ball, but we want you to find other options.*) Because if you have 150 and you use 150 on a ball, well then you have

zero left. If you don't want to get a football, what are some other things you could get? Think about it.

Most students began with Giovanny's question and figured out different ways to spend the 150 tickets. While many students successively subtracted quantities from 150 until all the tickets were spent (see figs. 3.3 and 3.4), others decided to spend only some tickets now so that they could spend the others later (see fig. 3.5). Students actively engaged in solving these tasks and comparing and justifying their solutions. Ms. Bustillos then invited several students to share their solutions with the group.

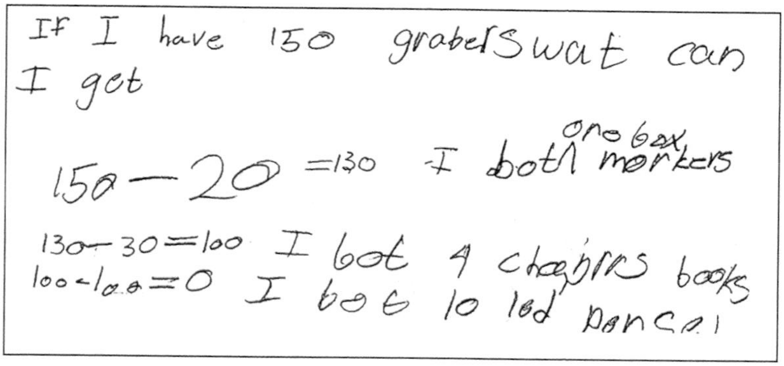

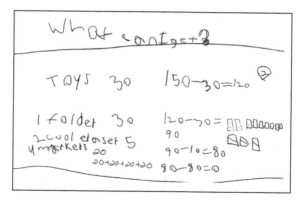

If I have 150 grabers wat can I got
$150 - 20 = 130$ I both ono box markers
$130 - 30 = 100$ I bot 4 chapins books
$100 - 100 = 0$ I bot 10 led Dancal

Fig. 3.3. Felipe's strategy: What can I purchase for 150 grabbers?

What can I get?
TOYS 30 $150 - 30 = 120$
1 folder 30 $120 - 30 = 90$
2 cool closet 5 $90 - 10 < 80$
4 markers 20
20+20+20+20 $80 - 80 = 0$

Fig. 3.4. Omar's strategy: What can I purchase for 150 grabbers?

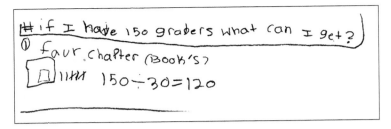

Fig. 3.5. Marisol's strategy: What can I purchase with 150 grabbers?

Making a Commitment to Access and Equity

Problem-posing discussions like the one in the opening vignette created opportunities for Ms. Bustillos's emerging bilingual students to draw on their experiences and interests to pose mathematical problems for the class to investigate. In this way, problem posing has the potential to facilitate key tenets of the Equity and Access Principle in *Principles to Actions: Ensuring Mathematical Success for All* (NCTM 2014). For instance, Ms. Bustillos frequently launched discussions using photos showing contexts that were familiar and relevant to students (see chapters 8 and 10). She typically took the photos herself, based on her knowledge of students' experiences and interests outside of school, but students, family members, or colleagues could also contribute photos. Ms. Bustillos then asked students to share what they noticed and wondered about as they viewed the photos. In this way, Ms. Bustillos was able to "leverage students' culture, conditions, and language to support and enhance mathematics learning" (NCTM 2014, p. 63). Although posing mathematical problems can be challenging for elementary grade students (English 1997), research has shown that grounding problem posing in relevant contexts is effective. For example, Turner, Varley-Gutiérrez, and Díez Palomar (2011) found that, for Latina/o bilingual elementary students, the experience of visiting familiar community locations such as a park or a donut shop and then discussing their observations and questions helped these students pose a range of mathematical problems about the settings. In fact, student-generated problems went beyond simple one-step calculations and reflected different operations and content areas. By encouraging students to mathematize familiar contexts, Ms. Bustillos was also deepening students' understanding of the relevance of mathematics in their lives. This practice is particularly important for students from historically marginalized communities, who often experience the school mathematics curriculum as disconnected from their lives and experiences (Civil 2002; Moll and Ruiz 2002).

Problem-posing mathematical discussions in Ms. Bustillos's classroom supported another key feature of the Equity and Access Principle (NCTM 2014).

These discussions "foster[ed] a sense of community that allows students to express their mathematics ideas . . . both orally and in writing, using the language of mathematics" (NCTM 2014, p. 66). In this way, problem posing supported language development by creating meaningful opportunities for students to use mathematical language (in Spanish and English) to pose questions and explain their reasoning. For Ms. Bustillos's emerging bilingual students, most of whom were Latina/o and came from bilingual communities that used both English and Spanish to communicate ideas, *bilingual* problem-posing discussions were particularly important because they allowed students to leverage both languages as resources (Moschkovich 2002, 2006).

Advancing Access and Equity

This section elaborates on specific features of problem posing that advance equity and access to mathematics for all students, and specifically for students from groups historically marginalized in mathematics. Each feature is illustrated with examples from Ms. Bustillos's second-grade bilingual classroom.

Students' Experiences Become Resources to Support Making Observations and Posing Questions to Investigate

Problem-posing discussions in Ms. Bustillos's classroom were grounded in authentic settings in the school and local community. We use the term *authentic* to refer to activity "that takes as its starting point the interests, perspectives, desires, and needs of the students" or their communities (Buxton 2006, p. 701). Research has shown that connecting mathematics to relevant and authentic experiences has the potential to increase students' interest and engagement and also to enhance students' learning (Civil 2007; González, Moll, and Amanti 2005; Simic-Muller, Turner, and Varley 2009). Specific to problem posing, grounding discussions in authentic settings allows students to use their experiences and understandings to make observations and to pose questions for the class to investigate.

For example, in another problem-posing lesson, Ms. Bustillos began by sharing pictures from a neighborhood *panadería* (bakery) that sold traditional Mexican cookies and *pan dulce* (sweet breads). This bakery, a long-standing establishment in the community, was frequented by many students and their families. When Ms. Bustillos presented the first photo of a case of cookies and sweet breads and asked, "¿Qué observamos aquí?" (*What do we notice?*), students immediately recognized the bakery and were eager to share their experiences. Students shared that the panadería sold tortillas, pan dulce, and cooking staples such as Mexican cheese and spices. When Ms. Bustillos asked students what they wondered about when they saw the photos, students used their knowledge of the context to pose and discuss a range of questions, such as these: ¿Cómo hacen las conchitas? ¿Por qué solo hacen estos tipos de galletas? ¿Dónde están los churros? (*How do they make the sweet breads? Why do they only make these kinds of cookies? Where are the churros?*). Ms. Bustillos recorded students' wonderings and then invited them to pose questions that they might be able to explore using mathematics.

Initially, some students struggled to pose problems that could be answered using mathematics. For example, some students' questions remained focused on methods for making certain pastries or whether specific types of items were sold. Ms. Bustillos had several strategies for supporting students in these instances, including referring students to a class anchor chart that listed possible "mathematical question starters" in English and Spanish (see fig. 3.2) and reminding students of mathematical questions posed in previous lessons. But most often, she turned students' attention to the context and asked them to think about the kinds of things that people might do in the setting or the kinds of questions that they would need or want to figure out. In this lesson, this move encouraged students to draw on their experiences at the bakery to help them pose problems and to share their ideas about solutions:

> Monica: ¿Hacen más conchitas o más cochinitos? Yo creo que más cochinitos porque son ricos. (*Do they make more of the shell-shaped Mexican sweet bread or the little pig-shaped cookies? I think more of the little pig-shaped cookies because they are really good.*)

> Anabel: ¿Si hacen 53 galletas y luego alguien compra 13, cuántas quedan? (*If they make 53 cookies and then someone buys 13, how many are left?*)

> Felipe: ¿Venden más donas o más churros? (*Do they sell more donuts or more churros?*)

Students shared that they thought the churros would be more popular.

In summary, by grounding problem-posing discussions in familiar and relevant contexts, Ms. Bustillos created opportunities for students to use their experiences to pose questions for the class to explore.

Students Pose a Broader Range of Problems than Are Typically Included in the Primary Grade Curriculum

When problem posing is based on authentic contexts that are genuinely of interest to students, students pose questions that they actually want to answer. These questions are not limited to particular mathematics content or standards, but rather are inspired by a situation that students want to understand better. In this way, when students' wonderings drive problem-posing activities, a broad range of problems often results (Turner, Varley Gutiérrez, and Díez-Palomar 2011). With primary grade students, this may mean that students pose problems that reflect content that is not a part of the formal curriculum until later grades (e.g., multiplication, division). However, since students' focus is not on specific operations but on making sense of the problems that they pose, they are generally able to solve these problems using a range of informal strategies, such as direct modeling (Carpenter et al. 1999).

As an example, later during the discussion about the neighborhood panadería, Ms. Bustillos presented a photo of a multilevel metal stand that displayed different flavors of Takis, a popular rolled tortilla chip snack (see fig. 3.6). While Ms. Bustillos had not planned to engage in a lengthy discussion about this particular photo, students were highly interested in the Takis display and immediately started sharing experiences and questions. They wanted to know what different flavors were sold and which flavors were most popular among customers. They posed questions such as these: ¿Venden más de los Takis verdes o de los Takis rojos?¿Cuántos más? (*Do they sell more green Takis or red Takis? How many more?*). Next, students started trying to count the number of Takis bags in the display stand, because they were interested in how many Takis one would have if the entire stand were purchased. These questions inspired a rich mathematical problem that students worked on for the remainder of the lesson: ¿Cuántas bolsas de Takis caben en los estantes? (*How many bags of Takis can fit in the stand?*).

Fig. 3.6. Takis stand in neighborhood panadería

To clarify the information needed to solve this problem, Ms. Bustillos asked students what they noticed about the number of Takis on each shelf. Students observed that there were four bags in the front row but that there were additional rows of Takis behind. Using what they could infer from the photo (some shelves were only partially filled, which made it easier to estimate how many rows of bags might fit on each shelf), students agreed that each shelf could probably fit three rows of Takis bags, with four bags in each row. Ms. Bustillos then asked students how many shelves there were in the stand: "¿Y cuántos estantes hay?" (*And how many shelves are there?*). Students then used this information (i.e., 5 shelves, and each shelf fits 3 rows of Takis bags, with 4 bags in each row) to figure out the total number of Takis bags that would fit in the display stand. Essentially, students were solving a multiplication problem involving three factors: (4 bags per row) × (3 rows per shelf) × (5 shelves in the stand). While Ms. Bustillos's students had not been formally introduced to multiplication, they generated a range of strategies to successfully solve this challenging problem (see chapter 4). For example, some students used a direct modeling strategy, drawing the display stand and then drawing 4 rows of 3 bags on each of the 5 shelves (see fig. 3.7). They then used various methods to find the total number of bags, including decomposing each of the 12s into a 10 and a 2 and then adding each set of quantities separately (see fig. 3.8). Other students built a model of one shelf using a drawing or counters (see fig. 3.9), and once they determined that each shelf held 12 bags, they used repeated addition to find the total (see fig. 3.10).

Fig. 3.7. Direct modeling strategy for
Takis Display Case task

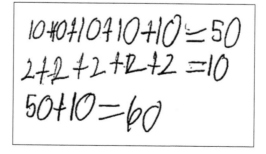

Fig. 3.8. Takis Display Case task,
decomposing strategy

Fig. 3.9. Takis Display Case task model,
one-shelf strategy

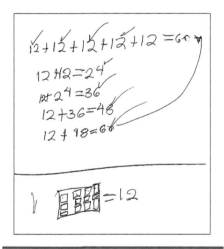

Fig. 3.10. Takis Display Case task,
repeated addition strategy

As another example, during a problem-posing discussion about a popular neighborhood pizza parlor, students posed a range of problems that included various operations and structures. After viewing photos of family parties or birthdays at the pizza restaurant, students came up with a range of problems related to setting up tables so that a large group could share and eat pizza. One student wanted to know if they used 5 tables with 8 people at each table, how many people would there be? Other students wondered about the games that the group could play while waiting for the pizza. Some of the problems that students generated included the following:

Ramón: How many slices of pizza are in 6½ pizzas? Each pizza has 8 slices.

Anabel: I have 100 tokens. I want to go on the roller coaster 5 times. It costs 4 tokens. How many tokens will I have left?

Mauro: There are 3 pizzas. Each pizza has 8 slices. I ate 8 slices, and my cousin ate 4 slices. How many slices do I have now?

In summary, we have found that when problem-posing discussions are grounded in authentic contexts, students pose problems that reflect a range of mathematical concepts and operations, which has the potential to enhance student learning.

Students Have Meaningful Opportunities to Use and Develop Mathematical Language in Both English and Spanish

Problem-posing discussions also provided students with meaningful opportunities to use and develop mathematical language. Initially, some students struggled to phrase questions that included mathematical problems to solve. In some instances, students' questions were narrated as stories that included the solution (i.e., I had 40 grabbers and then I spent 30 on notebooks and now I have 10 grabbers). To support students in phrasing questions that set up problems for the class to solve, Ms. Bustillos once again used a bilingual anchor chart that modeled different ways students might phrase mathematical questions in English and Spanish (see fig. 3.2). She referred to the chart during whole-group discussions and as she supported small-group interactions. For example, she commented:

> I love that [*the question about the photo*]. But let's see if we can come up with a math question. Here are some ideas to get us started. So you might ask [*pointing to the anchor chart*], ¿Cuántos? ¿Cuántos en total? or ¿Cuántos más necesito? or ¿Cuántos quedan? Or in English, you could ask questions like How many? How many in all? How many more do I need? Or how many are left?

Ms. Bustillos then asked students to think for a minute about possible questions and to share their ideas with a neighbor, providing another opportunity for students to practice phrasing mathematical questions. In addition, as illustrated in the opening vignette, once students posed a problem, Ms. Bustillos often turned to the class to ask students to restate the problem in their own words or to translate the problem to the other language. These ongoing opportunities to generate, hear, restate, and translate mathematics questions supported students' language development and their participation in mathematical discourse (Celedón-Pattichis and Turner 2012a).

In addition, when students posed questions that were incomplete or unclear, Ms. Bustillos worked with students to elaborate their ideas. This often involved a series of teacher probes and revoicing (restating students' ideas back to them so that they could hear, confirm, and possibly refine the idea) as Ms. Bustillos and the student collaborated to refine the problem. For example, during the grabber store lesson, one student wanted to know how many grabbers the store collected over the course of a school year.

Ms. Bustillos:	¿Quién tiene otra pregunta? (*Who has another question?*)
Roberto:	¿Cuántos grabbers usan cada año? (*How many grabbers do they use each year?*)
Ms. Bustillos:	¿Me puedes elaborar un poco más? (*Can you elaborate for me a bit more?*)
Roberto:	¿Cuántos grabbers usan los estudiantes? (*How many grabbers do the students use?*)
Ms. Bustillos:	Ah, quieres saber, ¿Cuántos grabbers utilizan los estudiantes cada año? ¿Qué más? (*Oh, you want to know, How many grabbers do the students use each year? What else?*)
Rodrigo:	En total. (*In all.*)
Ms. Bustillos:	Muy bien. ¿Cuántos grabbers utilizan los estudiantes cada año, en total? [*records problem on board*] A ver si Ms. G está llevando la cuenta. (*Very good. How many grabbers do the students use each year, in all? Let's see if Ms. G is keeping track.*)

Finally, when students shared their solutions at the end of each lesson, Ms. Bustillos used targeted probes to support students in explaining their thinking. Ms. Bustillos often extended these probes not just to the student who was presenting a solution but to the entire class so that all students could contribute to the discussions of the solution. For example, when Flor shared her solution for Giovanny's problem about what one could purchase for 150 grabbers, Ms. Bustillos invited all students to contribute to the explanation.

Ms. Bustillos:	Who got a different solution?
Flor:	I got 5 folders.
Ms. Bustillos:	Muy bien. ¿Y cuánto cuesta una carpeta? (*Very good. And how much does a notebook cost?*)
Flor:	5 folders. Each folder is 30.
Ms. Bustillos:	Vamos a ver si podemos calcular cuánto gastaste. [*to the class:*] ¿Qué debo de hacer, para ver cuánto gastó Flor? (*Let's see if we*

	can calculate how much you spent. What should I do to see how much Flor spent?)
Anabel:	Contar de 30 en 30. (*Count by 30s.*)
Ms. Bustillos:	A ver si lo podemos hacer todos juntos. (*Let's see if we can do it all together.*)
Students:	30, 60, 90 … 120, 150. [*Students count in unison in Spanish. Ms. Bustillos records quantities on the board as students count.*]
Ms. Bustillos:	A ver si podemos hacer la ecuación todos juntos. (*Let's see if we can write the equation all together.*)
Ramón:	30, más 30. (*30, plus 30.*) [*Ms. Bustillos records* 30 + 30.]
Ms. Bustillos:	¿Sigo? (*Do I continue?*)
Students:	¡Sí! Más 30, más 30, más 30. (*Yes! Plus 30, plus 30, plus 30.*) [*Ms. Bustillos finishes the expression* 30 + 30 + 30 + 30 + 30.]
Ms. Bustillos:	[*to Flor*] ¿Ahora cuántas carpetas tengo? (*Now how many folders do I have?*)
Flor:	Five.
Ms. Bustillos:	And what did you spend?
Flor:	All the 150.

In summary, Ms. Bustillos used bilingual problem-posing discussions to create meaningful opportunities for students to hear, generate, and develop mathematical language. These discussions fostered a sense of community among students where they were encouraged to share ideas and to collectively generate questions and problems for the class to solve.

Reflecting and Taking Action

In this section we outline several possible actions for getting started with mathematical problem posing grounded in authentic, relevant contexts in kindergarten through grade 2.

Talk to Students about Out-of-School Activities and Experiences

Ms. Bustillos used a variety of strategies to get to know students and to learn about their out-of-school experiences. For example, teachers might send surveys home at the beginning of the school year to find out about the students' and their families' interests (see chapters 2 and 10). In addition, we found class discussions or morning circle time to be an effective way to learn about places in the community that are familiar or of interest to students. Other strategies include inviting students to share photos of important family activities and inviting family members into the classroom to share their work or hobbies. Teachers can also use shared classroom experiences, such as a class field trip or a school festival, as the basis for a problem-posing discussion.

Gather Photos

We found the use of photos to be a very effective way to elicit young students' experiences and understandings about a context and to prompt them to ask questions or express wonderings. In our experience, it is useful to gather multiple photos that highlight different aspects of the setting. With young children, we have found that photos that illustrate activities, arrangements, and quantities are particularly helpful. For example, for the grabber store lesson, Ms. Bustillos prepared photos of baskets with different items for sale and the list of prices. For the pizza parlor lesson, she shared photos of families sharing pizzas, tables set up for birthday parties, and children playing various arcade games. A range of photos offers flexibility and allows students to share knowledge and experiences about aspects of the setting with which they are most familiar. It is important to note that the taking of photos may be prohibited in some communities or in certain community locations. Allowing students or families to bring in photos that they have gathered is a possible alternative.

Reflect on Mathematical Problems Related to the Photos

Prior to problem-posing discussions with students, reflect on possible mathematical problems related to the photos you have gathered. Think about different arrangements, measurements, groupings, or quantities in the photos and how they might inspire mathematical problems. Think about the activities depicted and the ways that mathematics might be involved in those activities. Reflect on your own wonderings about the photos and think about how those wonderings could be explored mathematically. As part of this reflection, consider any additional information that students might need to investigate the questions you brainstormed (or others). If possible, gather the information so that it can be shared with students as appropriate during the discussion. For example, for the lesson about the panadería, Ms. Bustillos had the list of prices for all items sold in case students generated questions about costs. In some instances, you may need to gather additional information after the initial brainstorming discussion with students. When this occurred in Ms. Bustillos's class, she simply told students that they would return to that problem during a subsequent lesson, once she gathered the information students requested.

Use Storytelling

Another way to prompt problem posing with elementary students is to ask students to tell stories about their after-school or weekend family and play activities. While one student shares a story, other students can make observations or pose questions that express wonderings. As when problem posing with photos, students can generate questions related to the student's story that can be explored mathematically. For examples, readers might consult Lo Cicero, Fuson, and Allexsaht-Snider (1999) and Celedón-Pattichis and Turner (2012b) for descriptions of their use of storytelling conversations to launch mathematical problems with young emerging bilingual students.

Closing Reflections

We found problem posing grounded in students' experiences and in relevant contexts from the school and local community to be a powerful way to support students' mathematics learning. Using both English and Spanish in these discussions was important, as it helped Ms. Bustillos's emerging bilingual students feel comfortable using either language, or both, to pose problems and to talk about their mathematical thinking. We close with a brief reflection from Ms. Bustillos on her experiences exploring problem posing with her students:

> This was truly an amazing experience for me as an educator, and I felt that I learned an enormous amount from my students during each one of these activities . . . more than in other lessons I'd taught throughout the year. I found that the engagement and participation of all learners was visible throughout. Students felt safe and confident in solving and posing problems they could relate to. Thanks to this, all learners felt they could participate in the task. In addition, I saw students solving problems that involved higher-level thinking (like the Takis task). To see this, and notice that students were not frustrated, but rather excited, was truly wonderful.

References

Buxton, Cory A. "Creating Contextually Authentic Science in a 'Low-Performing' Urban Elementary School." *Journal of Research in Science Teaching* 43, no. 7 (2006): 695–721. doi:10.1002/tea.20105

Carpenter, Thomas P., Elizabeth Fennema, Megan Franke, Linda Levi, and Susan Empson. *Children's Mathematics: Cognitively Guided Instruction*. Portsmouth, N.H.: Heinemann, 1999.

Celedón-Pattichis, Sylvia, and Erin E. Turner. "Case 1: Using Storytelling to Pose Word Problems in Kindergarten ESL and Bilingual Classrooms." In *Beyond Good Teaching: Advancing Mathematics Education for ELLs*, edited by Sylvia Celedón-Pattichis and Nora G. Ramirez, pp. 56–62. Reston, Va.: National Council of Teachers of Mathematics, 2012a.

———. "'Explícame tu Respuesta': Supporting the Development of Mathematical Discourse in Emergent Bilingual Kindergarten Students." *Bilingual Research Journal* 35, no. 2 (2012b): 197–216. doi:10.1080/15235882.2012.703635

Civil, Marta. "Culture and Mathematics: A Community Approach." *Journal of Intercultural Studies* 23, no. 2 (2002): 133–48. doi:10.1080/07256860220151050a

———. "Building on Community Knowledge: An Avenue to Equity in Mathematics Education." In *Improving Access to Mathematics: Diversity and Equity in the Classroom*, edited by Nailah S. Nasir and Paul Cobb, pp. 105–17. New York: Teachers College Press, 2007.

English, Lyn D. "The Development of Fifth-grade Children's Problem-Posing Abilities." *Educational Studies in Mathematics* 34, no. 3 (1997): 183–217. doi:10.1023/a:1002963618035

González, Norma, Luis C. Moll, and Cathy Amanti. *Funds of Knowledge: Theorizing Practices in Households, Communities, and Classrooms*. New York: Routledge, 2005.

Lo Cicero, Ana Maria, Karen C. Fuson, and Martha Allexsaht-Snider. "Mathematizing Children's Stories, Helping Children Solve Word Problems, and Supporting Parental Involvement." In *Changing the Faces of Mathematics: Perspectives on Latinos*, edited by Luis Ortiz-Franco, Norma González, and Yolanda De La Cruz, pp. 59–70. Reston, Va.: National Council of Teachers of Mathematics, 1999.

Moll, Luis, and Richard Ruiz. "The Schooling of Latino Children." In *Latinos: Remaking America,* edited by Marcelo M. Suárez-Orozco and Mariela M. Páez, pp. 362–74. Berkeley: University of California Press, 2002.

Moschkovich, Judit. "A Situated and Sociocultural Perspective on Bilingual Mathematics Learners." *Mathematical Thinking and Learning* 4, no. 2–3 (2002): 189–212. doi:10.1207/s15327833mtl04023_5

———. "Using Two Languages when Learning Mathematics." *Educational Studies in Mathematics* 64, no. 2 (2006): 121-44. doi:10.1007/s10649-005-9005-1

National Council of Teachers of Mathematics (NCTM). *Principles to Actions: Ensuring Mathematical Success for All*. Reston, Va.: NCTM, 2014.

Simic-Muller, Ksenija, Erin E. Turner, and Maura C. Varley. "Math Club Problem Posing." *Teaching Children Mathematics* 16, no. 4 (2009): 206–12.

Turner, Erin E., Maura Varley Gutiérrez, and Javier Díez-Palomar. "Latino/a Bilingual Elementary Students Pose and Investigate Problems Grounded in Community Settings." In *Latinos/as and Mathematics Education: Research on Learning and Teaching in Classrooms and Communities*, edited by Kip Téllez, Judit N. Moschkovich, and Marta Civil, pp. 149–74. Charlotte, N.C.: Information Age Press, 2011.

CHAPTER 4

Supporting English Language Learners in a Discourse Community

Nora G. Ramirez, *Nora Ramirez Consulting, Tempe, Arizona*
Socorro H. Tapetillo, *Galveston Elementary School, Chandler (Arizona) Unified School District*

At the beginning of the school year, Socorro Tapetillo was puzzled about how to help her second-grade students, all English language learners, engage in mathematical discourse. She was especially concerned about Mario, a student in the school since kindergarten, because his previous teachers and his parents told her that he would not speak in either English or Spanish. Mario received special services because of his lack of speech. He had been labeled "Special Ed"—a move that disturbed Socorro. She knew that some labels can negatively affect students and can be difficult to remove.

Socorro noticed that when Mario was engaged in mathematics, he successfully used manipulatives to solve problems and would often give the answer to a question, but only whispered it to himself. As a veteran teacher, she was aware of his whispering and jotted Mario's whispered answers on the board along with the answers of others, with the intention of enticing him and all the students in discourse. Although the rest of the class did not whisper, these second graders' talk consisted of guesses, short phrases, or staring at Socorro in hopes that she would give them an explanation or the answer. The students were content with waiting for her and had not yet attained the skill of reflecting on their thinking and sharing their thoughts. Socorro knew she had to foster and facilitate a mathematics discourse community (Celedón-Pattichis and Ramirez 2012; Willey 2010), a classroom in which students contribute to mathematical conversations, make sense of mathematics, learn to use precise language to publicly explain their mathematical thinking, and listen to and build on the conversations of others.

When thinking specifically about Mario and his whispering, Socorro began to wonder, "Is he not speaking aloud because he can't or is it because he won't?" After all, Mario did whisper, which meant he was *able* to talk. She also wanted to know, "How can I get Mario to look at his partner when I ask partners to talk? How can I help Mario feel more comfortable talking aloud and explaining his thinking?" All but one of the students in Socorro's class needed to do this, but Mario had the most to grow in this area. Mario lacked confidence, which affected his ability to communicate his mathematical thinking.

While reading *Mindset: The New Psychology of Success* (Dweck 2006), Socorro began to develop ideas of what she needed to do. She wanted to change her students' ideas of what they think "smart is." They thought that if you get answers quickly in mathematics then you are smart. She wanted her students to learn that being smart means persevering when they encounter something difficult and, through effort, make progress and learn. She also wanted them to learn that making mistakes makes them smarter (Boaler 2016). This was not going to be an easy task. Another book—*Elephants Cannot Dance!* (Willems 2009)— came to Socorro's rescue! Socorro read this book to her class with the intent of developing a class with a growth mindset and to emphasize that effort and mistakes can lead to learning. She wanted her students to change their ideas about the meaning of failure, smartness, and the importance of effort.

After discussing the book, the class and teacher created a personal effort chart (see fig. 4.1) to describe the goal and levels of performance relative to that goal (Marzano 2007). Socorro's students participated in describing personal effort behaviors related to becoming smarter and then assigning behaviors for each numeral on the scale. Recording the students' language on the chart reinforced their use of explicit descriptive language. The chart was constructed by gathering students' comments on questions such as "Why did you decide that you should have a 0 on the personal effort chart?" In the summary of a lesson, in addition to focusing on the mathematics of the lesson, the students used this chart to reflect on their behaviors, thus developing more responsibility for their learning. For example, after students shared and discussed their work to an addition story problem, Socorro asked them to review the personal effort chart and to share their scores. When reporting out, Mario whispered "0" for his score. Socorro told him, "When you whispered your answer, you were not at a 0 anymore. It showed that you tried." Mario then whispered, "1." With time, Mario began to talk aloud. Mario, who was once a whisperer, even volunteered to be the narrator of the second-grade play, which was intended to give students experiences in talking aloud. Socorro says,

> Mario taught me how to create the environment the whole class needed to become a learning community. He was labeled as a student with special needs until the spring. Now, he no longer has to leave my classroom except for speech therapy. Mario now talks aloud and is an ongoing contributor to our mathematics discourse community.

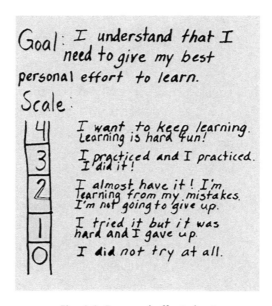

Fig. 4.1. Personal effort chart

Making a Commitment to Equity and Access

The second-grade classroom in the vignette above is in Arizona, a state that separates English language learners from other students and requires ELL students to participate in four hours of language instruction. Arizona Proposition 203, 2000 legalized instruction in English only, and the subsequent Arizona Department of Education's research-based Structured English Immersion (SEI) models require that ELL students receive a minimum of four hours per day of English language development (ELD) (Arizona Proposition 203 2000; State of Arizona Department of Education 2014). These laws ban students from learning in their native language, deny ELL students equitable opportunities to discuss and make sense of mathematics, and leave a limited amount of time for students to acquire instruction in mathematics and other content areas. Teaching within this context, Socorro is committed to a classroom that promotes access and equity as described in *Principles to Actions: Ensuring Mathematical Success for All* (NCTM 2014) by making accommodations so that her students have an excellent mathematics program with high expectations and support, in order to maximize the learning potential of each student.

Several obstacles are associated with Arizona laws for educating ELL students, their segregation from non-ELL students, the lack of self-confidence resulting from that segregation, and the lack of high expectations, normally associated with children who are English language learners or live in poverty. To overcome these obstacles and achieve equity and access in mathematics, educators must have productive beliefs (NCTM 2014). Having beliefs is easy; enacting those beliefs when teaching is not.

Working within the Arizona laws, Socorro strategized goals and activities to achieve equity and access in mathematics within her classroom. She focused on building the students' self-confidence and sense of community, having students learn English while learning mathematics, leveraging their language and culture, and consistently supporting all aspects of their mathematics learning at grade level (NCTM 2014). She has an extensive professional library that guides her in learning and implementing effective mathematics teaching practices. Her beliefs, expectations, and interventions are indicative of her efforts to achieve equity and access for her English language learners.

Socorro believes that her students can learn, and she was determined that they would believe this too. She worried that students who are tracked either by ability or by level of knowledge of English may develop a lack of self-confidence. As we read in *Principles to Actions* (NCTM 2014):

> Even more disturbing is the lack of self-confidence that far too many students develop and that leads them to view mathematics as something that is far beyond their grasp and that they can never hope to understand. . . . Furthermore, educators may reinforce this misconception by sorting students by ability, believing that some can "do math" and others cannot. (p. 62)

Socorro was concerned that her students might assume that they are not smart, since they were placed in a special class in order to learn. This lack of confidence, which is manifested in students' thinking that they cannot learn, negatively affects their learning experiences and must be addressed.

Using the Growth Mindset research (Dweck 2006), Socorro focused on shifting her students toward a growth mindset, knowing that she still needed to acquire more skills in facilitating this change in her classroom. The classroom charts supported the students in this movement by requiring them to apply growth mindset goals to their learning experiences and to use language as they did this. After completing mathematical tasks, students used the scales to determine their scores, shared the scores, and read the appropriate description in the class. When reflecting on what they did to keep learning, students were asked to state their thought in a complete sentence, such as "Today I asked for help from _____ so I could keep learning." Forming and stating complete sentences is an instructional strategy for teaching English language learners.

In addition to reflecting on their efforts to complete mathematical tasks and to reinforce the productive belief that all students are capable of achieving in mathematics, Socorro asked the students to begin to use the word *yet*. With Socorro's prodding, students might say, "I do not know how to do it *yet*." Intertwining growth mindset ideas and language development with the mathematics learning was essential for students to be mathematically successful.

Lack of self-confidence was also manifested in the students not talking or engaging in discourse. Believing that their lack of engagement did not indicate a lack of knowledge, Socorro realized that they needed experiences in speaking publicly, so she decided that the students would participate in a play. This activity would require them to speak in front of others while also learning that it was acceptable to make mistakes. The play was a support that they needed to be successful. It helped them overcome the discourse hurdle of fear of talking in front of others, and it led them to develop the skills they needed to eventually express their mathematical ideas, including learning to hear and accept critiques (which often occur in a mathematics discourse community) and working together to achieve a common goal. Thus, the play supported the growth of a sense of community in the classroom.

Advancing Equity and Access

Socorro teaches in a Title 1 school where 97 percent of the students are Latinas/os. All her students are English language learners, ranging from the beginning to the intermediate stages of language development. Socorro was born in Mexico and moved to Arizona when she was very young, so she is familiar with the kinds of experiences, confusions, excitements, and frustrations of being an English learner. Having worked as an accountant for twenty years, she is comfortable with mathematics; teaching mathematics has always been of great interest to her. Since she began teaching, she has been on a journey to effectively differentiate and meet the varied mathematical needs of her students. Following are details on instructional strategies and tools that she uses to advance equity and access to mathematics, an essential element of an excellent mathematics program (NCTM 2014).

Ongoing Assessments and Differentiation

Socorro uses both diagnostic and formative assessments throughout the instruction sequence. She uses the results not to track students into ability groups but to guide instruction and heterogeneously group students to foster collaboration, communication, and learning. Since learning English while learning mathematics is of utmost importance, communication considerations are always at the forefront of instructional decisions. Her students work at kidney tables because she observed that kidney tables encourage collaboration and discourse among her students. She considers who should sit next to whom, differentiating according to language and mathematical needs. She employs small-group instruction to facilitate differentiation and to address gaps in mathematics with grade-level goals in mind. At the beginning of the school year, Socorro made considerable effort to develop the students' confidence and skills to participate in a mathematics discourse community by having them be actors in a play.

A Play

Recognizing that her students appeared uncomfortable when people looked at them or paid any attention to them, Socorro conceived the idea of having her students participate in a play. She knew that the students would be willing participants because they could connect a play to their cultural ways of storytelling (Turner et al. 2009), thus leveraging their culture to support their learning (NCTM 2014; see chapters 2, 3, 8, and 10). Socorro wanted her students to realize that it is important that people hear them when they talk; but at the same time, she knew that in order to build their self-confidence they needed to feel comfortable with what they had to say. A play was the perfect avenue to achieve that.

The play, an enactment of *The Three Silly Billies* (Palatini 2005), was chosen because of all the connections that could be made to mathematics and engineering, such as counting money, applying geometrical concepts, and building bridges. It was intentionally presented in an area close to the classroom, a comfortable environment where family and students would be at ease.

To reduce their anxiety level, students self-selected their roles in the play; thus, several students had the same role and memorized the same lines. Having to read scripts and memorize lines affected their reading skills and also reinforced learning the structure of English sentences. The play was performed three times; after each performance, the students had to communicate with others about their roles. They began to use one another as resources. For example, when the Trolls were practicing their lines, Julia was watching and said, "When you say that, you need to open your hands and say it like this, '**Who** is crossing my bridge?'" Julia, a quiet girl who, by choice, had no lines in the play, helped her classmates by observing and offering constructive feedback. She emerged as a leader and took on the role of director in the second performance of the play. As a result of giving and receiving critique, the students began to develop the language skills they needed in their mathematics community: those of asking questions, listening to and contributing to mathematical conversations, and building on what others had to say. At the end of each performance the students reflected on their experiences. One student said,

> I learned to speak loud for [sic] the people could hear me. I learned not to laugh when people are speaking. I should be listening because you learn more from other students. I learned to not be shy because if you are shy the people are gonna think that you don't know anything.

Another student said, "I was shy because I didn't want people to see me. Now I am not shy. I want people to see me . . . I want to explain math." A third student shared, "I was scared because I think [sic] I will say a word wrong but I got them right. It is a lot of work."

It is not often that a teacher uses a play with the goal of increasing mathematical communication. The play was an intervention that worked by leveraging students' culture, conditions, and language to support mathematics learning (NCTM 2014). Another intervention that worked was developing a growth mindset in the students.

Growth Mindset

The book used to introduce a growth mindset, *Elephants Cannot Dance!* (Willems 2009), involved Piggy, who wants to teach Gerald, the elephant, to dance. Gerald is hesitant because he says that elephants cannot dance. Gerald wants to make Piggy happy, so he continues to practice even though it is difficult. He feels like a failure until two squirrels ask for dance lessons, not from Piggy, but from Gerald. Through all the practice and mistakes he had made, Gerald had learned to dance. Reading and discussing this book was the first step in changing the second-grade students' ideas of failure, smartness, and the importance of effort.

In addition to developing the personal effort chart (see fig. 4.1), Socorro gathered comments from small groups of students on what they needed to do to keep learning, developed a draft anchor chart as groups shared, and finalized a class chart based on their ideas (see fig. 4.2). It is important to note that, at times, Socorro uses small groups when gathering information in order to ensure that all students have an opportunity to contribute and be heard.

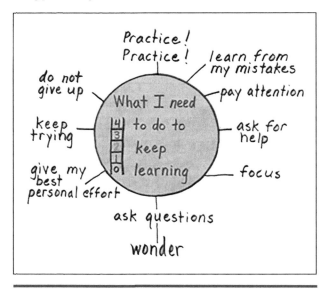

Fig. 4.2. Supporting a growth mindset

Prior to the classroom emphasis on growth mindset ideas, when Mario gave a response and it was incorrect, he would cry. Thus, Socorro learned to engage the class in celebrating the risks Mario took in giving an answer and recognizing that Mario's incorrect response had created learning opportunities for both him and the class. His mistake resulted in a class discussion that allowed students to think differently and to solve a problem in a different way. Now, Mario proudly calls his incorrect responses "learning mistakes." Socorro says, "His learning mistakes and the mistakes of others continue to give all of us, myself included, opportunities to learn." The students now know that with effort they can do something that they could not do before. They now confront challenges with persistence. They are learning what it means to be smart. Socorro has learned to celebrate mistakes and publicly praise effort and perseverance. The anchor chart shown in figure 4.2 was developed to address behaviors related to learning. Socorro typically uses anchor charts to focus on mathematics.

Anchor Charts

Socorro uses anchor charts daily to highlight conceptual understanding, mathematical tools, strategies, representations, and student language as well as precise mathematical language (see chapter 5). In an ELL classroom, it is imperative that anchor charts be created and made public during instruction to emphasize the value of students' contributions. Pre-made anchor charts do not achieve this goal, but classroom-generated anchor charts lead to student understanding and ownership of the contents of the chart. They are the support that students need to be successful (NCTM 2014). Figure 4.3 shows an anchor chart that Socorro used in a lesson focused on place value, the result of a preassessment that revealed issues with students reading and writing numbers beyond 120. The students read 403 as "forty-three" and wrote 4003 when Socorro said "four hundred three." To address issues of reading and place value, she developed the chart and engaged the students in completing it, attending to the mathematics concepts and the mathematical language. Note that the bottom part of the anchor chart is not complete because the students had not yet engaged in a discussion of counting back from 456 when the photograph of the chart was taken. The folds in the paper indicate that this section was not displayed while the counting-on discussion was occurring. Anchor charts are also used to focus on the problem-solving process and are especially important when teaching ELL students because of the language issues associated with reading and interpreting problems.

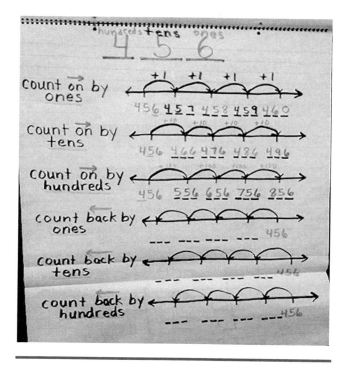

Fig. 4.3. Place value anchor chart

Problem Solving

To give her students opportunities to learn English while learning mathematics, Socorro centers her mathematics class on solving word problems using common addition and subtraction situations (see CCSSM, Mathematics Glossary, table 1, NGA Center and CCSSO 2010). Socorro often replaces numbers with a blank line so that students concentrate on reading and understanding the context of the problem, the first step in solving a problem.

Solving Javier and Sylvia's dollars: A glimpse into the classroom. The students individually read the problem (see fig. 4.4) and begin to solve it using manipulatives, visual representations, or numbers. The teacher walks about, asking clarifying questions and noting observations. Some students are digging in while others are unsure of what to do. Enough time is allotted to allow students time to make sense of the problem but not enough so students who are unsure of what to do flounder for an excessive length of time.

> Javier has 47 dollars. Sylvia has 18 more dollars than Javier. How much money does Sylvia have?

Fig. 4.4. Javier and Sylvia's dollars

Then the students gather in a circle on the floor with Socorro seated by the chart stand. The discussion begins in this way:

T:	Would someone like to read this problem?

[*A student reads the problem.*]

T:	What is this problem about?
S:	Javier and Sylvia. [*The teacher draws representations of them.*]
T:	What do you know about Javier and Sylvia?
S:	They have money.
T:	Who has money?
S:	Javier and Sylvia have money. [*The teacher draws dollar signs with blanks.*]
T:	Do you know anything else? Talk to your partner and tell them what else you know.

[*Discussion ensues for less than a minute.*]

T:	So, what else do you know?

S: Sylvia has more money than Javier.

T: What tells you that?

S: It says it right here. Sylvia has __ more dollars than Javier.

[The teacher uses the chart (see fig. 4.5) as a reference to summarize what they know.]

T: Now, what does the problem ask you to find? Turn to your partner and give the sentence you would write to answer this question. Make sure you use the units in your answer statement.

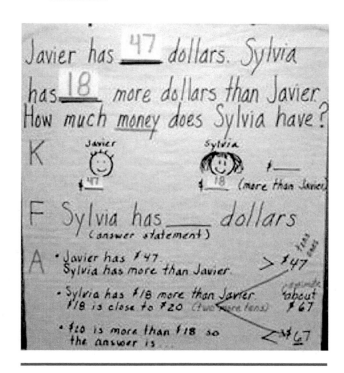

Fig. 4.5. KFA anchor chart

[One or more students share an answer statement, e.g., Sylvia has __ dollars. The teacher records the students' contributions, then displays the numbers.]

T: Talk to your partner about what you now know about this problem. Without working the problem, what can you say about the answer? [*Points to the answer statement and reads it.*] What do you know about the number that is in the blank?

[The students begin sharing using complete sentences.]

S: Sylvia has more than $47.

[After the student defends the statement correctly, the teacher records ">$47" by the answer statement on the chart.]

S: Sylvia has about $67. Because $18 is close to $20.

[Teacher records "about $67."]

T: I want you to talk to your partner. [Student] said that Sylvia has about $67. Decide if Sylvia has more than $67 or less than $67.

After students share their thoughts and final estimations are recorded, the students solve the problem. Using a document camera, three students present their work showing tape diagrams, number lines, and numbers. They compare their answer statement to the recorded estimates. Other students ask questions of the student presenters. The teacher highlights the different strategies and tools that the students used.

The process that Socorro used in the problem-solving vignette described above is called the KFA process (see fig. 4.6). Instead of picking out numbers in a word problem and performing operations with little thinking, students need to read and understand the language, make sense of the context, and participate in mathematical discourse. The K asks students to determine what they **know** about the situation. The F refers to what the problem is asking them to **find**. The A refers to what they know about the **answer**, not give the answer. When using the KFA process before solving a problem, it is not unusual for students to exhibit most of the Standards for Mathematical Practice (NGA Center and CCSSO 2010). Often, giving estimates of the answer is more rigorous than performing operations because it requires both number and operational sense. The KFA process gives the potential for students to engage in higher order thinking and for raising the mathematics achievement of all students (NCTM 2014).

While KFA is an effective process for solving problems, there are other considerations when giving word problems to ELL students, especially those at the beginning stages of language development (Celedón-Pattichis and Ramirez 2012). These considerations include the use of object visuals and, if possible, cognates to support these students in interpreting a word problem. Using word problems is an effective tool to deliberately engage students in learning English while learning mathematics (NCTM 2014).

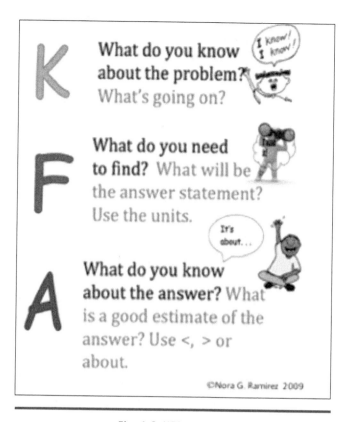

Fig. 4.6. KFA process

Students Learning English While Learning Mathematics

Socorro reinforces language while teaching mathematics. Marisa, a monolingual student who joined the class in the third quarter of the school year, had language needs that most of the other students no longer had. When problem solving in mathematics, Socorro chose to include her in understanding the problem by using cognates and picture clues to facilitate her reading.

When the class was working the Farm Animals problem (see fig. 4.7) with their individually assigned numbers, Socorro chose to differentiate by having Marisa put 13 in the first blank and 7 in the second blank. Socorro purposefully chose 13 because it sounds like *trece* ("thirteen" in Spanish) and 7 because it is similar to *siete* ("seven" in Spanish). She chose to give a problem that had at least one cognate (animals-*animales*) so Marisa would feel success as she read. Socorro planned to give her the same problem with more challenging numbers after she was able to read and comprehend the problem.

> There were ___ animals on the farm. ___ were
> horses. The rest were cows. How many were cows?

Fig. 4.7. Farm Animals problem

To begin, Socorro asked Marisa to read the problem. Then she said to Marisa, "Explain the problem. ¿Entendiste lo que dije?" (*Did you understand what I said?*). Marisa replied, "¿Quiere que le explique el problema?" (*Do you want me to explain the problem to you?*). Socorro now knew that Marisa comprehended the instructions. Marisa was able to say that the problem is about animals (animales), and Socorro used pictures to help her understand the words *horses* and *cows*.

Marisa reads beyond grade level in Spanish, and Socorro was intent that Marisa recognize and appreciate that her Spanish can be useful in learning English and in doing mathematics. Not only does Socorro want to nurture Marisa's identity, she intentionally wants

> to instill in her that she does not need to wait for me or a student
> to be able to read and understand. I want her to recognize that her
> personal effort makes a difference in what she learns. I want her to
> recognize that her language is an asset. I will be there to support
> her, but she does not need me every step of the way. I know that not
> speaking English does not equate to a lack of knowledge.

Socorro also gives Marisa opportunities to act out problem situations, listen to other students explain and model with mathematics, sit next to someone who speaks both Spanish and English and maybe code switches, not because she needs a translator, but because she needs opportunities to listen, converse, and ask questions of her teammates.

The examples shared above describe some of the different instructional strategies and tools that Socorro uses to foster and support a classroom environment that consistently promotes access and equity. Whether using ongoing assessments, small-group instruction, a play, a growth mindset focus, anchor charts, or mathematical problem-solving, the mathematical goals are aligned to grade level standards and there is always an emphasis on learning English while learning mathematics.

Reflecting and Taking Action

What does a teacher do when her students are from another culture or speak another language? In reflecting on this question, Socorro realizes that in some ways it is easier for her to develop an effective classroom environment because she shares the same language and a similar culture with her students. She knows to refer to soccer instead of football. She can say "¡Tu trabajo duro valió la pena" as easily as she can say "Your hard work paid off!" She can interact with parents with little effort. She is aware of cognates that she can use in story problems to support students in reading, and she is familiar with the algorithms that the parents use when they help their children.

She shares what she might do differently if her students spoke a language other than Spanish and invites readers to consider these actions when teaching students whose first language is different than theirs.

- Incorporate more pictures during instruction, while solving word problems, and on the anchor charts.

- Determine if the student's language shares cognates with English. If so, use them as much as possible.

- Intentionally support students' positive identity regarding both language and culture (Aguirre, Mayfield-Ingram, and Martin 2013). For example, have students read and write in their first language and use translating software to read their work.

What does a teacher need to know and do when using anchor charts in a mathematics class? Socorro feels very strongly that a teacher should pre-plan the components of an anchor chart and complete the chart with the students. She says,

> When planning an anchor chart for a single mathematical idea, I consider the conceptual understanding or procedural fluency I want students to develop, the related common misconceptions and mathematical language, and the graphics that I will use to represent these ideas. I also decide on the questions I will ask to stimulate student thinking and the numbers I will use to elicit productive struggle during the class discussions. All these decisions are based on what students already know and my interpretation of how to get them to the next level of mathematical understanding.
>
> I recognize the importance of acknowledging the contributions that all students make in a discussion and have learned to include incorrect thinking on a chart, anticipating that the erroneous thinking will be uncovered by its contributor or [by] a peer. Discussing erroneous thinking in class is no longer a sensitive issue because the students know that their brain grows when they make a mistake.

When anchor charts are consistently produced, the result can be an abundance of them. Categorizing and managing these charts so they can be used as a reference when needed can be overwhelming. Socorro suggests taking pictures of the charts and using the digitized charts as reference. In addition, copies of the charts can be given to students, and they can place them in their mathematics journals or interactive notebooks to refer to as needed.

The reader is encouraged to use anchor charts when teaching mathematics. Socorro says, "Just get started. My charts are not always perfect, some are a work in progress, i.e., we keep adding onto them, and some just need to be refined or redone." What is most important is the mathematical message of the chart and engaging the students in its development. Strive for sound mathematics, precise language, powerful graphical representations, and student ownership (see chapters 1, 2, 3, and 5). Note that each of these elements improves with experience.

Are the benefits of telling stories and participating in a play worth the added time and effort? To achieve equity and access, students must be convinced that they have a voice. If students are expected to exhibit the Standards for Mathematical Practices and contribute to a mathematical learning community, they will need to recognize that what they have to say is important and can make a difference in their learning and the learning of others. When English language learners are asked to talk or contribute to mathematical discussions, they experience both cognitive demands and emotional demands. The cognitive demands require them to think about what they know mathematically and how to express that knowledge. However, the emotional demands involve fear of producing the language correctly, lack of self-confidence in what one has to say, and the fear of speaking in front of others. Socorro says, "While I chose a play to address my students' lack of talk, I now know from the students' reflection that the play reduced the emotional demands that occur when students are asked to speak."

Considering the successes gained from the play, readers are asked to reflect on their students' engagement in class discussions and determine if some students may not be contributing because they do not feel they have a voice. Giving students experiences in hearing themselves speak without cognitive demands may address hidden emotional issues tied to speaking in front of others. This can greatly affect students' participation in a mathematics discourse community.

References

Aguirre, Julia M., Karen Mayfield-Ingram, and Danny Martin. *The Impact of Identity in K–8 Mathematics Learning and Teaching: Rethinking Equity-Based Practices*. Reston, Va.: National Council of Teachers of Mathematics, 2013.

Arizona Proposition 203 2000. English Language Education for Children in Public Schools Act. https://ballotpedia.org/Arizona_English_Language_Education_for_Children_in_ Public_Schools,_Proposition_203_(2000) (accessed on March 15, 2016).

Boaler, Jo. *Mathematical Mindsets: Unleashing Students' Potential through Creative Math, Inspiring Messages, and Innovative Teaching*. San Francisco: Jossey-Bass, 2016.

Celedón-Pattichis, Sylvia, and Nora G. Ramirez. *Beyond Good Teaching: Advancing Mathematics Education for ELLs*. Reston, Va.: National Council of Teachers of Mathematics, 2012.

Dweck, Carol S. *Mindset: The New Psychology of Success*. New York: Ballantine Books, 2006.

Marzano, Robert J. *The Art and Science of Teaching*. Alexandria, Va.: ASCD, 2007.

National Council of Teachers of Mathematics (NCTM). *Principles to Actions: Ensuring Mathematical Success for All*. Reston, Va.: NCTM, 2014.

National Governors Association Center for Best Practices and Council of Chief State School Officers (NGA Center and CCSSO). *Common Core State Standards for Mathematics*. Washington, D.C.: NGA Center and CCSSO, 2010. www.corestandards.org/

Palatini, Maggie. *The Three Silly Billies*. New York: Simon & Schuster Books for Young Readers, 2005.

State of Arizona Department of Education. "Approved Refinements to the SEI Models." https://cms.azed.gov/home/GetDocumentFile?id=55257a811130c008a0c55bd4

Turner, Erin E., Sylvia Celedón-Pattichis, Mary Marshall, and Alan Tennison. "'Fíjense amorcitos, les voy a contar una historia': The Power of Story to Support Solving and Discussing Mathematical Problems with Latino/a Kindergarten Students." In *Mathematics for Every Student: Responding to Diversity, Grades Pre-K–5*, edited by Dorothy Y. White and Julie S. Spitzer, pp. 23–41. Reston, Va.: National Council of Teachers of Mathematics, 2009.

Willems, Mo. *Elephants Cannot Dance!* New York: Hyperion Books for Children, 2009.

Willey, Craig. "Teachers Developing Mathematics Discourse Communities with Latinas/os." In *Proceedings of the 32nd Annual Meeting of the North American Chapter of the International Group of the Psychology of Mathematics Education,* edited by Patricia Brosman, Diana B. Erchick, and Lucia Felvares, pp. 530–38. Columbus: Ohio State University, 2010.

CHAPTER 5

Equity and Access to the Complexity of Number

A Multimodal, Digital Approach

Rebecca Cohen, *Braemar Elementary School, North Vancouver, British Columbia*

Sean Chorney and Nathalie Sinclair, *Simon Frasier University, British Columbia*

Three grade 1 children, all of whom have been struggling with numbers in their regular classroom activity, are sitting together with their teacher, sharing a single iPad. They have been working on "friends of ten" (complements in ten) using the TouchCounts iPad app (Jackiw and Sinclair 2014). Their teacher, Ms. Cohen, plays a game in which she creates a number, say six, by touching six fingers on the screen simultaneously, which makes a "herd," or a group, of six small circles in a disc on which the numeral 6 appears (see fig. 5.1) and which prompts the iPad to say "six." The children must create the complement of that six to make ten, then pinch the two herds together (a gesture that combines those herds into one on the screen).

Ms. Cohen begins by making a herd of six and invites Kristie to take the first turn. All the children watch as she touches her fingers to the screen. (All student names are pseudonyms. Note: The app's audio was in French; Cohen sometimes spoke in French as well.)

Kristie:	[*places four fingers on the screen*]
TouchCounts:	Quatre. (*Four.*)
Kristie:	[*pinches the herds of six and four together*]
TouchCounts:	Dix. (*Ten.*)
Ms. Cohen:	OK, Armando, c'est ton tour. (*OK, Armando, your turn.*)
[*Ms. Cohen makes a herd of three.*]	
Armando:	[*places eight fingers together on the screen*]
TouchCounts:	Huit. (*Eight.*)
Dolores:	You made eight!
Armando:	[*pinches the herds of three and eight together*]
TouchCounts:	Onze. (*Eleven.*)
Armando:	One too many. [*takes one out of the herd of eleven*]
TouchCounts:	Dix. (*Ten.*)

Photo by Dale Northey SFUCreative

Fig. 5.1. After having made a herd of
six, the child prepares to create another
herd

Dolores, who has been watching attentively, quickly moves the herd
of one that was taken out by Armando to the side of the screen. Now
there are two herds of ten on the screen. Ms. Cohen then makes a herd of
two and invites Dolores to take the next turn. The game continues, with
the children successfully making complements in ten of one, six, seven,

eight, four, and three. As the herds of ten accumulate on the screen—there are now nine of them—the children express a desire to combine all of the herds together, saying, "Let's make a really big number!"

Ms. Cohen:	What will you get if you put them all together?
Dolores:	Two tens together makes twenty!
Ms. Cohen:	Interesting. What will three tens together make?
Armando:	Thirty.
Ms. Cohen:	What about four tens?
Armando:	Forty.
Ms. Cohen:	What will nine tens make together?
Dolores:	Ninety.
Ms. Cohen:	Make another ten.
Armando:	[makes one herd of size nine and another of size one and then pinches them together]
TouchCounts:	Dix. (Ten.)
Ms. Cohen:	What will you get if you put the ninety and the ten together?
Armando:	Tenty?

Ms. Cohen writes 100 on a piece of paper and says, "This is what tenty would look like. Do you know what that number is called?" Dolores exclaims, "It's a hundred!" Armando pinches the herds of ninety and the ten together and makes a herd of size one hundred. All three children begin to cheer, saying, "A hundred, a hundred, a hundred."

Making a Commitment to Access and Equity

We would like to highlight two features of this vignette that connect to the Access and Equity Principle in *Principles to Actions: Ensuring Mathematical Success for All* (NCTM 2014):

> An excellent mathematics program requires that all students have access to a high-quality mathematics curriculum, effective teaching and learning, high expectations, and the support and resources needed to maximize their learning potential. (p. 5)

The first feature relates to high expectations that Cohen, the teacher, has for these children as she engages them in high-quality tasks, even though they have been struggling with more basic ones, such as recognizing, reading, and writing numbers. In the vignette, Cohen follows the children's interest in making a big number and structures their play so that they attend to multiples of ten. She expects them to work with larger numbers and helps them use the pattern in the number names to generate thirty, forty, ninety, and a hundred. (Armando's "tenty" shows nicely how he has picked up on the structure of the number names and how, by repeating that word, Cohen validates his thinking.) When the children want to make big numbers, which they find very exciting, she invites them to do so in a way that also enables them to continue to practice necessary curriculum skills. Thus, the children are engaged in productive *and* pleasurable practice, where the practice is subordinated to the more challenging task of making a hundred, which in turn enables them to attend to place value.

The second feature relates to the particular resource that is being used in this vignette, which has several affordances that we believe support the maximizing of children's potential. One affordance is the direct feedback the app provides on children's actions. When Armando accidentally made a herd of size eleven instead of ten, for example, he could not only see and hear that he had not made ten, but he could also self-correct (by taking one away from the eleven). This nonjudgmental environment, we hypothesize, encourages children to try actions, to make some mistakes, and to learn from the feedback, without becoming dependent on the teacher's authority.

Another affordance is the multimodal nature of the app. When using TouchCounts, children see a visual representation both of number (the six circles in the herd) and of a numeral (6), hear the number name spoken ("six"), and feel their six fingers tapping the screen. The children in the vignette, who have explored numbers with this app before, show that they know the complement in ten of three by stretching out seven fingers simultaneously and placing them on the screen. Their tangible expression of seven, which can be seen as a kind of gestural subitizing (which involves visually and quickly evaluating the number of elements in a collection without counting them), offers a way of knowing through the fingers in an environment where the gesture is then associated with both a numerical symbol and a number name.

In the next section, we offer four short episodes from our ongoing research that illustrate further the two main features of access and equity we have highlighted above. We will also use these additional vignettes to show the way in which the teacher's work with the three children enabled them to engage collaboratively with powerful mathematical ideas and demonstrate their mathematical thinking in various ways, permitting the teacher to assess what they knew. We will also address what we deem to be unproductive beliefs in relation to access and equity that concern children's use of their fingers in learning how to count and do arithmetic. Instead of seeing the use of fingers as a crutch that needs to be taken away as soon as possible, we point to recent neuroscience research that supports the use of fingers as tools that are both dependable and useful for engaging with mathematically rigorous and challenging tasks. Indeed, TouchCounts can be seen as providing an environment that both encourages finger use and extends its power.

Advancing Access and Equity

In this chapter, we focus on three children with distinct learning profiles. They are part of a French immersion grade 1 class with twenty-four students in total. These children (Armando, Dolores, and Kristie) were chosen to work in a small group with Cohen, their classroom teacher, two to three times a week over eight weeks for twenty minutes at a time, because although they were able to count up to ten and to identify numerals 1 to 10, they still struggled with several aspects of number sense, including identifying numbers between eleven and twenty, particularly in French; figuring out partner numbers to ten; and correctly predicting which number is one after or one before a number between five and twenty. All three students were at the beginning stage of French language development, and English was their native language. Armando's father also frequently spoke to him in Spanish at home, though Armando tended to respond to him in English. Therefore, instead of asking students to do the usual morning mathematics in their individual workbooks, Cohen worked with them in a small group either in the classroom or in the hallway, and they spoke in a combination of French and English. The rest of the children continued with the morning routine while Cohen worked with Armando, Dolores, and Kristie. There was a full-time educational assistant in the classroom who worked with the rest of the children.

Description of the Students and Their Learning Profiles

Armando was generally quiet and easygoing. He was cooperative and eager to contribute knowledge as well as assist the other children in the intervention group. Armando had difficulty processing verbal information in order to follow through on the instructions. For example, if he was asked to take a sheet of paper, walk to his desk, and write his name on the page, he would often walk over to his desk without retrieving the paper, and then sit and watch the other children begin their work. He did not seem to realize that he was doing something different from his peers and would sit until asked again to go and get the paper. Cohen thus repeated instructions frequently and tried to offer visual cues. Armando was still developing his fine motor skills and thus had trouble printing letters and numbers on paper.

Kristie was a very motivated student who worked hard on tasks assigned to her. She was always asking questions to learn more about mathematics. However, like Armando, she was still developing her ability to recognize number symbols and had difficulty remembering information. She sometimes became anxious when she did not understand how to do something. For example, if the instructions were not clear to her, she would often go to Cohen in tears.

Dolores was a lively student who was good at connecting what she was learning with prior knowledge; her strong verbal skills supported explaining her thinking in the small-group setting. She had not attended kindergarten, and this had led to difficulties adjusting to school during the first part of the year. She had trouble paying attention and staying on task. Through the first months of the year, she also struggled with following group instructions and expectations. She was placed in Cohen's French immersion grade 1 class, and the language challenge made her transition to school even more difficult. Dolores was artistic and skilled when it came to drawing and to seeing patterns and symmetry; however, she did not learn to print properly before coming to school and was still developing the ability to print lowercase letters and number symbols.

All three children seemed to require much repetition: Armando for his difficulties in processing, Kristie for retention, and Dolores for learning the language. Two of the primary reasons Cohen chose to use TouchCounts as part of the intervention were its built-in language support and the way it facilitates productive and pleasurable practice.

A Brief Description of TouchCounts

TouchCounts is a free, multi-touch iPad app that is primarily intended for counting but can also be used for adding and subtracting (Jackiw and Sinclair 2014). The app contains two main microworlds, both of which are available in English, French, and Italian. Counting happens in the Enumerating World, where a user taps her fingers on the screen to summon numbered objects (yellow discs) in turn. The first tap produces a disc containing the numeral 1. Subsequent taps produce successively numbered discs. As each tap summons a new numbered disc, TouchCounts "speaks" the corresponding number word in the language that has been selected. Through repetition of touching, a child becomes part of the mathematics she or he is creating, for it is in the repetition of continued summoning that the mathematics (ordinal numbers, for example) are brought into existence. Number as a concept becomes more than seeing a symbol or speaking a sound—it is a creation based in a physical act of repeated touching.

Fingers can be placed on the screen one at a time or simultaneously. With five successive taps, for instance, five discs (numbered 1 to 5) appear sequentially on the screen and are announced by being counted aloud, one by one, as they appear. However, if the user places two fingers on the screen simultaneously, two consecutively numbered discs appear at the same time, but only the higher-numbered one is named aloud ("two," if this is the first tap). The discs always arrive in numerical order, with their symbolic names imprinted on them.

If the "gravity" option is turned on within the Enumerating World, the numbered object holds its position beneath the learner's fingertip as long as her finger remains pressed to the screen. But as soon as she lifts her finger, the numbered object "falls" and disappears off the bottom of the screen. The gravity option includes the option of a "shelf," a horizontal line across the screen. If a user releases the numbered object above the shelf, it falls only as far as the shelf and comes to rest there, rather than vanishing from sight. (Figure 5.2 depicts a situation in which there have been four taps below the shelf—these numbered objects were falling—and then a disc labeled "5" was placed above the shelf by tapping above it. See the YouTube video "Putting 10 on the shelf," TouchCounts 2015b.)

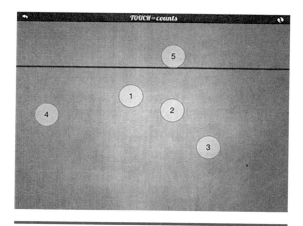

Fig. 5.2. The screen after four sequential taps
below the shelf and then a fifth tap above it

While tapping on the screen in the Enumerating World creates sequentially numbered objects, tapping on the screen in the Operating World creates autonomous numbered sets, which we refer to as "herds." The user places one or several fingers simultaneously on the screen, an action that immediately creates a large disc encompassing all the fingers (as in the vignette, when Kristie made four). When the fingers are lifted from the screen, the numeral is spoken by the app, and the smaller discs are then lassoed into a herd and arranged regularly around the inner circumference of the big disc (fig. 5.3a shows two herds, of ten and of four). After two or more such arrangements have been produced (as in fig. 5.3b), they can be pinched together (addition) or "unpinched" (subtraction or partition). The new herd is labeled with the associated numeral of the sum (see fig. 5.3c), which TouchCounts announces aloud. Moreover, the new herd keeps a trace of the previous herds, which can be seen by means of the differentiated colors. (See the YouTube video "Number Compositions," TouchCounts 2015a.)

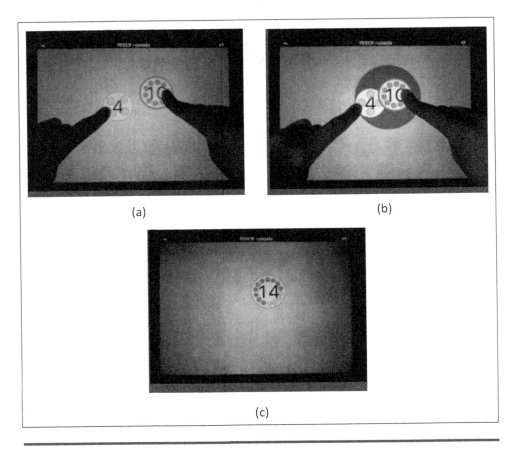

(a)

(b)

(c)

Fig. 5.3. (a) The herds of 10 and 4; (b) pinching two herds together; (c) the result of the pinched herds becomes a herd of its own, with a color trace of the two herds

In our studies with three- to five-year-olds (preschool), as well as five- to seven-year-olds (kindergarten and grade 1), we have been particularly interested in how the "shelf" provides children with an opportunity to move beyond counting in a singsong manner and to begin to attend to the relation between number words (what comes before ten, what comes after four, etc.), which is a necessary part of developing number sense (see Sinclair and Heyd-Metzuyanim 2014). We have also examined the following aspects of children's activity with TouchCounts: finger gnosis (Sinclair and Pimm 2015b), gestural subitizing (Sinclair and Pimm 2015a), attention to symbols and place value (Coles and Sinclair 2017), and the rhythmic basis of counting and skip counting (Sinclair, Chorney, and Rodney 2016).

Working toward Access and Equity with TouchCounts

In the next four subsections, we look closely at four aspects of Cohen's work using TouchCounts with the children that provide insights into the way we think access and equity were achieved.

Access to reading and writing symbols. Cohen most often used TouchCounts alongside small portable whiteboards on which the students wrote numerals and made diagrams. For example, Armando created two herds of five with his fingers and pinched them together. Dolores and Kristie then wrote the equation representing this action on their whiteboards: 5 + 5 = 10. Then Dolores used the iPad while Kristie and Armando wrote on their whiteboards. In one episode, Dolores made a herd of two on the screen and pinched it with the herd of eight that had been placed there by Rebecca. Armando watched intently, then wrote 8 + 2 = 10 on his whiteboard before the herds were pinched together, thus producing the sum himself.

Armando would not have been able to do this as easily had the children been using ten frames, for example, or other, similar manipulatives such as Cuisenaire rods or counters, because these manipulatives do not have number symbols on them. In contrast, TouchCounts offers students the opportunity to work directly with the symbols, through tactile, visual, and auditory feedback. These features provided support for the students because they could refer to the symbols on the screen as they wrote their equations on their whiteboards. This support was especially important in regard to the numeral 2, which the children had previously had trouble writing and distinguishing from 5.

The importance of this feature is underscored by recent neuroscience research showing that skilled symbolic numerical magnitude processing is correlated with achievement in arithmetic (Vanbinst et al. 2016) and that symbolic ordinal processing predicts success at higher levels of mathematics more generally (Lyons et al. 2014). TouchCounts provides access to this powerful way of engaging with number. We hypothesize that Armando, Kristie, and Dolores would have had trouble developing adequate fluency with symbols by working only with manipulatives and that this would have put them even further behind in grade 2 (and onward), where pencil-and-paper arithmetic is done primarily through symbols.

Fingers: Counting with and counting on. Once the children had worked on "complements in ten" over a period of time, they became quite fluent at finding the correct complement and also at writing down the corresponding equation. Indeed, they frequently wrote the left side of the equation before the pinching action had been made on the screen. We look more closely at one episode in which a herd of four was on the screen, and it was Kristie's turn to complete the complement. Kristie stretched out her fingers on both hands, palms down, curled four fingers on her right hand, said "six," and placed her six outstretched fingers on the screen. She did this same kind of gesture three more times when Cohen asked her for the "friends" (complement) of three, two, and one.

Kristie was successful at finding each of the complements, but what is significant is how she used her fingers to communicate her mathematical thinking. At the beginning of the students' work together, Kristie was not able to identify the correct complements unless the first number was five or nine, the complements most often suggested during whole-class discussions on complements in ten. But after the intervention, during which complements in ten were worked on frequently, she seemed to have learned how to use her fingers both to help her identify the correct complement and to express her thinking. Furthermore, in watching Kristie's actions, Cohen could see that Kristie was actually carrying out a form of subtraction, since she was stretching out her ten fingers and then curling up (or taking away) the number of fingers corresponding to the number shown on the screen.

Most significant, Kristie was not taking away her fingers one by one (curling her fingers one at a time), but taking them away all at once. This suggests that Kristie was thinking about number as cardinal quantity, which enabled her to "count on" as well as to add and subtract. The fact that she used her hands with the palms down strongly suggests that she had learned to use her fingers in this way through her interactions with TouchCounts (children typically count on their fingers with their palms facing up). Her finger use, however, could also enable her to solve arithmetic problems in the absence of TouchCounts.

For Kristie, the physical, finger-based action provides a way of thinking about complements in ten that is quite different from a ten frame, which relies on visual and spatial perception. She could use her finger-based action to help remember the number words and reason through the problem.

While mathematics education research sees finger-based counting and calculating as needing to be replaced by more abstract representations—the prevalence of this belief has recently been countered by Boaler's (2016) support for the use of fingers in mathematics learning—we note that the neuroscience literature indicates "a functional and beneficial interrelation between fingers-based numerical presentations and numerical/arithmetical development in terms of embodied numerosity representation" (Moeller et al. 2011, p. 77). Based on our work with Armando, Dolores, and Kristie, we believe that finger-based strategies may be especially important in terms of access and equity because they provide alternative modes of expressing and manipulating numbers that are always accessible and easily shareable.

Action-based explanations of mathematical conceptions. TouchCounts provides students the opportunity to communicate through number words and number symbols and through actions and gestures, thus providing a multimodal approach to representing mathematical thinking (see chapters 3 and 4). Students are able to describe what they notice about numbers and the actions they use to produce a result. This aspect was quite apparent when Armando, Kristie, and Dolores explained, for example, how to skip count. When skip-counting by fives, the children would use four fingers placed below the shelf and one placed above it in order to generate 5, 10, 15, . . . on the shelf, with the corresponding auditory sequence "four, five, nine, ten, fourteen, fifteen, . . . " from the app (see fig. 5.4).

After Kristie had done this type of skip counting, Cohen asked if there was a pattern, to which Kristie responded, "There is [*sic*] four on the bottom one on the top, four on the bottom one on the top, four on the bottom one on the top . . . " She continued until Cohen asked her whether there was a pattern in the symbols, and Kristie observed, "It's a five and then a zero, then a five and then a zero." Kristie had become aware of the numerical pattern of counting by fives; and through the action of putting four fingers below the shelf and then one above, she also had begun to attend to how every fifth number is written and verbalized, which she was able to explain. In line with a high-quality mathematics program, Kristie reconceptualized skip counting as a physical, rhythmic, four down and one up pattern, but also as a symbolic pattern of alternating 5s and 0s for the digits in the ones place.

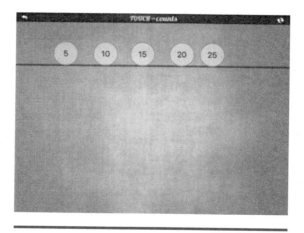

Fig. 5.4. Skip-counting by fives in TouchCounts

Furthermore, when the children were asked to predict what would happen when two herds were pinched together, they would sometimes pinch their fingers together in the air, as if recreating the gesture they had made when using TouchCounts. After making such a gesture, the children could successfully provide a response. The action they had learned using TouchCounts enabled them to articulate a mathematical operation in a singular yet accessible way. Given the challenges that Armando and Kristie had in terms of remembering verbal information, we hypothesize that their growing success in mathematics was based on the greater facility they had for remembering actions, such as gestures for pinching or the "subitizing gesture" for cardinal quantities and, in the excerpt described above, the rhythmic, skip-counting action.

Repetition. One affordance of TouchCounts that we have mentioned in passing is the way in which it demands and invites repetition. *Repetition* is not used here in the sense of "practice makes perfect." Rather, we are talking about repetition as an act of participating in the opportunities and potentials of TouchCounts: It is less of a requirement and more evidence of engagement. Repetition was evident in the opening vignette, when the children made many herds of ten.

In another example, Kristie skip-counted by two by placing only even numbers on the shelf. After she put discs numbered 2, 4, 6, 8, and 10 on the shelf, she hit the reset button and said, "I want to try again." She did the same thing again but kept the numbers closer to each other so that she could go further (that is, she made more room on the shelf). She ended up putting the even numbers up to 30 on the shelf and stopped only because she had reached the edge of the screen. Her repetition was not to practice but to engage in constructing more mathematical objects, in this case even numbers to 30.

Students can become demotivated if asked to repeat a set of exercises again and again; but Kristie wanted to continue building the pattern for the sake of building the pattern and thereby reaching larger numbers. Hewitt (1996) uses the term *subordination* to refer to the way that practicing a simpler skill (in this instance, making complements) can be deployed in the service of accomplishing a more challenging and interesting mathematical task (e.g., making one hundred). Fluency may be developed, but the student's attention is on the larger goal. This aligns with the repetition afforded in TouchCounts, where the practicing does not feel mechanical and attention can be on higher-level mathematics.

Obstacles and Challenges

As with any classroom teaching task or tool, TouchCounts can create challenges for a teacher. First, when using the application, young children can inadvertently touch the screen with more or fewer fingers than they had intended, which can cause confusion. Children may also struggle to manipulate herds on the screen.

TouchCounts is most effective when children share one iPad in a small group, because discussion arises and children have the opportunity to see different ways of completing a task through their peers' work. For some children, however, this type of small-group work can be a challenge. When it is not their turn, they sometimes lose focus (in the intervention described in this chapter, Dolores walked away from the group several times when it was not her turn); some children may also be reluctant to share the iPad or participate in any sort of group work.

Earlier, we discussed how gestures helped the children learn; indeed, for Dolores, Kristie, and Armando, gestures were an integral part of remembering and communicating their thinking. For example, when asked to generate even numbers, Armando was very efficient in the tapping sequence necessary to place all the even numbers up to 20 on the shelf. This does not mean that Armando understood the concept of even number—for this, further tasks and discussions would be necessary. Indeed, Armando was not able to consistently make an even number when working in the Operating World. This discrepancy gave Cohen an insight into Armando's developing understanding of evenness.

In addition to the challenges inherent in the use of the app, the "pull-out" model of the intervention has benefits and drawbacks. When using this type of intervention, the timing and the setting need to be considered. Cohen often started the day with a mathematics lesson or discussion and then gave students time to work in individual workbooks. The intervention group met during the workbook practice. Ideally, students would be pulled out during a subject in which they had fewer difficulties or could be caught up at a later time. However, Armando, Dolores, and Kristie were still able to partake in the daily morning mathematics lesson or discussion before they left to do their small-group work; and as these students generally required extensive help with their math workbook, Cohen decided that using TouchCounts in a pull-out situation would be valid use of time and would not lead to a deficit in mathematics instruction for these students. The students taking part in the intervention did not see the app as a resource only for those struggling with mathematics because Cohen had used the app on several occasions with the whole class. Indeed, several of the students who were not pulled out asked frequently to join the group.

The pull-out model was effective for the setting. When the three children met with Cohen in the hall, they could hear the spoken numbers more easily than in the noisier, whole-classroom setting. Hearing the numbers is a significant affordance of TouchCounts, especially in a bilingual environment.

A potential drawback of the pull-out intervention is that it took students away from their peers up to three times a week. Because these students also received literacy intervention four times a week, they missed a good deal of class time.

Because of the benefits and drawbacks of a pull-out intervention, this model should be carefully considered when creating accessibility for students.

Reflecting and Taking Action

In this chapter, we have provided examples of the numerous affordances of TouchCounts and how using this technology inspired children to engage in exploring number. In addition to seeing the number symbol, they were supported in their engagement by a one-to-one correspondence using their own fingers, a voice from the app that said the number aloud, and the visual support of discs with number symbols appearing on the screen. Teachers need to consider how each of these modes of working with number might support different learners. It is also important to help children attend to each of these modes. A teacher might ask children to close their eyes so that they attend to the audible numbers, for example, or ask them to draw a hand making 3 on the screen so that they attend to the actions of their fingers.

These aspects of TouchCounts invited children to engage in high-quality mathematics because they were not held back by having to focus always on computation. They could reach large numbers quite easily and attend to patterns, such as when Armando counted to and tried to name the number 100 or when Kristie described skip counting by 5 in two different ways. Given young children's penchant for large numbers, teachers must think carefully about how to pose questions and direct attention so that creating large numbers in TouchCounts leads to productive mathematics. This might require a delicate balance between letting the children explore, marveling at the big numbers, and intervening with more directed requests and challenges. Cohen found that the use of the whiteboards was effective in slowing down the children's actions on the screen and enabling them to reflect on what they had produced by writing their numbers or making drawings of what they had done.

Armando, Kristie, and Dolores all made gains through their work with Cohen and TouchCounts. Their fluency with numbers became apparent in other classroom situations. For example, shortly after the intervention sessions had ended for the year, Cohen asked Armando to take ten counters from a bin. He took a handful, counted them, and said, "I have eight." When Cohen asked how many more he needed, he replied, "Two," without hesitation. Through working with TouchCounts, Kristie became adept at counting on, both by using her fingers and with counters, and also at solving arithmetic equations. Dolores filled some gaps in her learning that she had missed in kindergarten by mastering the number word sequence in French up to twenty.

These gains were supported by the use of TouchCounts, but also by the additional time these three children had to work with their teacher. As a result of the intervention, Cohen herself came to understand the particular ways these children had of understanding number better. The question remains, however, whether pulling children out of class is the most equitable approach. Might it be possible to devise a classroom environment in which pulling out was not necessary?

TouchCounts is an open-ended and non-goal-oriented mathematical application. For the app to be used most effectively, a teacher or some other knowledgeable person needs to help guide students, and prompts and problems must be provided that might be quite different from those used with other manipulatives. Asking children to compute sums when TouchCounts can give the answer may not be an effective use of the app. Asking children for different ways of making ten, however, focuses attention less on the sum and more on number composition. How might a teacher evaluate the productiveness of a problem? One important criterion would be whether children can use the feedback provided by TouchCounts in order to help them solve the problem. In order to use the feedback, children must also learn how to attend to the various modes—visual, auditory, and touch—provided by TouchCounts. How might teachers help make these forms of feedback explicit while continuing to engage children in high-quality mathematics?

Finally, we would like to highlight the importance of small-group work. In each episode, because the children worked in pairs or groups of three, they often shared the iPad. This aspect of turn taking provided an approach that supported equal opportunity, because the representation of number or pattern became more than a construction of one student. There was an equitability in the final mathematical result because it was based on the contributions of all the children involved. This multisharing approach, along with the affordances of TouchCounts, provided an accessibility to number for all children both individually and socially.

References

Boaler, Jo, and Lang Chen. "Why Kids Should Use Their Fingers in Math Class." *The Atlantic*, April 13, 2016. https://www.theatlantic.com/education/archive/2016/04/why-kids-should-use-their-fingers-in-math-class/478053/

Coles, Alf, and Nathalie Sinclair. "Re-thinking Place Value: From Metaphor to Metonym." *For the Learning of Mathematics* 37, no. 1 (2017): 3–8.

Hewitt, Dave. "Mathematical Fluency: The Nature of Practice and the Role of Subordination." *For the Learning of Mathematics* 16, no. 2 (1996): 28–35.

Jackiw, Nicholas, and Nathalie Sinclair. *TouchCounts*. Application for the iPad, 2014.

Lyons, Ian M., Gavin R. Price, Anniek Vaessen, Leo Blomert, and Daniel Ansari. "Numerical Predictors of Arithmetic Success in Grades 1–6." *Developmental Science* 17, no. 5 (2014): 714–26.

Moeller, Korbinian, Laura Martignoon, Silvia Wessolowski, Joachim Engel, and Hans-Christoph Nuerk. "Effects of Finger Counting on Numerical Development: The Opposing View of Neurocognition and Mathematics Education." *Frontiers in Psychology* 2, no. 328 (2011): 75–78.

National Council of Teachers of Mathematics (NCTM). *Principles to Actions: Ensuring Mathematical Success for All.* Reston, Va.: NCTM, 2014.

Sinclair, Nathalie, Sean Chorney, and Sheree Rodney. "Rhythm in Number: Exploring the Affective, Social, and Mathematical Dimensions of Using *TouchCounts*." *Mathematics Education Research Journal* 28, no. 1 (2016): 31–51.

Sinclair, Nathalie, and Einat Heyd-Metzuyanim. "Learning Number with *TouchCounts*: The Role of Emotions and the Body in Mathematical Communication." *Technology, Knowledge and Learning* 19, no. 1–2 (2014): 81–99.

Sinclair, Nathalie, and David Pimm. "Whatever Be Their Number: Counting on the Visible, the Audible, and the Tangible." In *Integrating Touch-Enabled and Mobile Devices into Contemporary Mathematics Education*, edited by Maria Meletiou-Mavrotheris, Katerina Mavrou, and Efi Paparistodemou, pp. 50–80. Hershey, Pa.: IGI Global, 2015a.

———. "Mathematics Using Multiple Sense: Developing Finger Gnosis with Three-and Four-Year-Olds in an Era of Multi-touch Technologies." *Asia-Pacific Journal of Research in Early Childhood Education* 9, no. 3 (2015b): 99-109.

TouchCounts. "Numbers Compositions." TouchCounts.ca video, 3:22. September 28, 2015a. https://www.youtube.com/watch?v=oJxdNJlHBNk

———. "Putting 10 on the shelf." TouchCounts.ca video, 1:22. September 28, 2015b. https://www.youtube.com/watch?v=7xD-pqnsce0

Vanbinst, Karin, Daniel Ansari, Pol Ghesquière, and Bert De Smedt. "Symbolic Numerical Magnitude Processing Is as Important to Arithmetic as Phonological Awareness Is to Reading." *PLoS One* 11, no. 3 (2016). https://doi.org/10.1371/journal.pone.0151045

Developing Advocacy for Equitable Approaches to Teaching Mathematics from Within

Maura Varley Gutiérrez and Georgette Abouattier Blay, *Elsie Whitlow Stokes Community Freedom Public Charter School, Washington, D.C.*

The parents gathered around the long tables in the library of the prekindergarten through fifth-grade language immersion public charter school where students learn content in French and English or in Spanish and English. They were eager to share some of what they had just observed in their children's mathematics classroom during the remaining part of our mathematics Open Classroom event. Prior to the classroom observation, school instructional leadership had provided an overview of the curricular approach (teaching mathematics for understanding), and after the observation of their children's mathematics classes, families were getting ready to reflect on their observation with teachers and ask questions. Some parents remarked that they could follow what was happening, even though the lesson was being conducted in French or Spanish. Other parents shared that they were not necessarily able to follow or were confused by the strategies students used to solve mathematics problems because they had learned different approaches.

Our work to implement both APTT meetings and home visits is generously supported by the Flamboyan Foundation: flamboyanfoundation.org.

However, they were impressed that the students were able to explain their thinking and to come up with an accurate answer. Parents also commented on the length of time it took some students to solve a problem, even if it was correct and the strategy worked for that student. Other parents commented on the level of engagement that students showed, which, they emphasized, was in a mathematics class no less!

One parent in particular took on the role of advocate for teaching mathematics for understanding and also talked about the kind of support parents can provide to their children in this "new" way of doing mathematics. She spoke passionately about how she had struggled with what to do to help her son, how she had taken a step back and tried something new, imploring other families to do the same. Below is that parent's testimony about her experience:

> Growing up, math was a difficult subject for me but I got it. So when my son, Adonis, came with math homework, I wanted him to do things the way I learned. I found myself struggling in the beginning because my son was doing things in a different way. After a few tries and watching him, I asked him to show me what he could do. He started doing math in a very different way; surprisingly to me, the results were correct. I told him to keep going and he did. When I checked everything, it was all right. I told him to do as he learned in school and I would only check after he was done and so I did.

This parent, whom we will call Carolina, had learned to trust her son's strategy choice; and although it does not necessarily come across in these words as written on the page, she spoke with great passion to other parents in the Open Classroom session, which she reflects upon here:

> [After the classroom visits in the Open Classroom], the teachers explained what the kids were doing and learning in class. Some parents started talking about the frustration they were experiencing at home trying to help with homework. I told them then about my experience with Adonis and what I have been repeating for the last few years in these meetings, "Let your kids do it and only check that they did." I have also found very helpful using the *Investigations* [student math] book [TERC 2008] that students get every year as support not only for them but for us parents to be involved. I have learned a couple of strategies myself, too. The books are a great tool for parents that learned the traditional way.

Carolina noted that while her child is doing mathematics homework, she lets him approach the problem in his own way and uses curricular resources to be able to understand his strategies, which differ from traditional methods. Although she says "only check" when describing her role in supporting her son, she then expands upon her role to discuss learning new strategies herself instead of trying to intervene and insisting on the strategy she knew. After Carolina shared this shift in her support of her son, a feeling of relief and determination spread throughout the library. A fellow parent who understands the struggle with homework that involves new and unfamiliar methods and with trying to understand what is best for her own children is a valuable advocate to help bring about a shift in thinking within a school building. Carolina's words, rather than those from a school administrator, helped other parents feel reassured and empowered to try a new approach to supporting their children.

If we are to bring about change within schools that are attempting to provide equitable mathematics schooling experiences, advocacy is essential (Legnard and Austin 2014). In this chapter, we will argue how this advocacy relates to equity; provide an overview of the approaches that we took to develop advocacy within our teachers, parents, and students for teaching mathematics for understanding; and offer advice for others who wish to be successful in shifting the way mathematics is taught and learned at their schools.

Making a Commitment to Access and Equity

The Access and Equity Principle from the NCTM's *Principles to Actions* states: "An excellent mathematics program requires that all students have access to a high-quality mathematics curriculum, effective teaching and learning, high expectations, and the support and resources needed to maximize their learning potential" (NCTM 2014, p. 5). In theory, who could argue with those words? Of course we want all students to have access to good curriculum, good teachers, and the resources needed to learn and for all students to be held to high expectations. However, who defines what is a high-quality mathematics curriculum and effective teaching in mathematics? This is contested ground, and the Common Core State Standards (NGA Center and CCSSO 2010), while fraught with issues such as developmental inappropriateness of some of the grade-level placement of standards and unfunded mandates related to roll-out, have the potential to provide a larger audience for advocating for teaching mathematics for conceptual understanding and high-quality mathematics curricula that promote this approach. It is increasingly important to develop advocates for teaching mathematics for understanding so that the most crucial aspects of the Common Core State Standards (CCSS) are not lost in the next political wave.

However, because little outreach has taken place around teaching mathematics for conceptual understanding and the connections to the standards, a movement of negative association with what is colloquially called "Common Core math" developed and continues to grow. Greater emphasis on standardized testing, the transition for many states to the CCSS (NGA Center and CCSSO 2010) and accompanying Next Generation Assessments, and increased emphasis on showing immediate gains with growth data have put pressure on parents, students, teachers, and districts to make changes in their mathematics programs. These changes offered an incredible opportunity to bring about widespread reform; unfortunately, they have been met with backlash and, at times, outrage. (See, for example, comedian Louis C.K.'s tweets railing against the Common Core and standardized testing [D'Addario 2014].) Much of this backlash is fueled by the rough transition to Next Generation Assessments and accompanying fear and anxiety. As often happens in the world of education, the dangerous narrative that "Common Core math" is confusing and is leading our children toward mathematical failure as compared to other countries (see Garelick 2012 for an example of this kind of narrative) influences decisions about curriculum, teaching approaches, and parent involvement, at best (Herbel-Eisenmann et al. 2016). At worst, it reinforces notions that poor children and children of color need "traditional" or back-to-basics approaches to teaching that still permeate our educational landscape (Nieto 1992), and it most certainly counters the Access and Equity Principle. The successful implementation of a curriculum aimed at developing conceptual understanding could prove indispensable to bringing to scale the elements in the CCSS related to teaching mathematics for understanding, which are critical to implementing the Access and Equity Principle and ensuring the educational success of all students in mathematics. In order to do this, we need to develop advocates for the approach among all stakeholders, including parents such as Carolina, whose words opened this chapter.

Advancing Access and Equity

We will now describe the avenues that we (Georgette Abouattier Blay as a teacher lead, Maura Varley Gutiérrez as the director of teaching and learning, and other members of our instructional support team) have taken in our school community in order to foster a successful mathematics program focused on developing conceptual understanding (which we believe allows us to hold high expectations and provide a high-quality mathematics program to our students), including developing expertise in teachers to forge partnerships with parents in support of our approach.

This partnership with parents proved essential in preparing our students to feel confident, comfortable, and engaged with our mathematics curriculum; and while engaging parents is not explicit in the Access and Equity Principle, they are important stakeholders in our students' lives. After adopting a student-centered curriculum focused on building conceptual understanding, we soon realized that, in order to best support our students, we needed to engage our families in learning about this curricular approach alongside us.

We began the transition from an unclear curriculum tending toward traditional to the curriculum Investigations in Number, Data, and Space (TERC 2008). We provided support for teachers in order for them to truly embrace a student-centered curriculum focused on building conceptual understanding. Teachers were introduced to the curriculum and provided with professional development on the idea that there is a progression of strategies for problem solving in different content areas and a student-centered approach to teaching mathematics, generally. After almost a whole year of using the curriculum, teachers began believing in the approach of the Investigations curriculum. Students were explaining their thinking and were highly engaged in mathematics practices, and students of multiple abilities were demonstrating conceptual understanding. However, teachers began reporting that their students were faced with a dilemma: Do I solve problems in ways that make sense to me and are supported by my teacher, or do I solve problems in the way that my parents are showing me at home? In addition, parents reported frustration with "slow" or "confusing" methods of teaching key grade-level skills. Families shared their frustrations in parent-teacher conferences or in passing conversations and questioned these methods. They showed genuine and justifiable concern that teachers were setting up their children to be judged harshly after elementary school or to not be competitive in the world outside of our school (particularly with using strategies that are slower than using an algorithm or because of the decreased emphasis on speed in solving problems). To paraphrase the concerns of one parent: "I worry about how my African American son will be judged by the outside world if he is using a method that is inefficient." This mother was reminding us that because of the additional societal barriers faced by students of color, it was even more essential that we develop families as advocates for the methods being used by her son and by the many other students of color in the school.

As our teachers became advocates for teaching mathematics for understanding, we soon realized that it would be even more effective, and we would ultimately strengthen the trust that our families had in our school, if we engaged families in learning about a student-centered approach to mathematics based on developing conceptual understanding. The school already had a strong family engagement program that included home visits to begin the year in order to form deep relationships with families, showing students and families that their knowledge is valued and integral to the school (González, Moll, and Amanti 2005).

Building on this program, we started integrating family engagement strategies around mathematics. The following section outlines our learning as we developed programs to engage our families and the specific strategies we employed and to which Carolina referred in our opening vignette. These included Open Classrooms, content-based family mathematics sessions and family meetings centered on sharing assessment data about problem solving, and home activities to support key grade-level skills.

Open Classrooms

In our first effort, which we called "Open Classrooms," families were given an overview of teaching mathematics for understanding by instructional support team members, invited to observe a mathematics lesson in their children's class, and then debriefed with teachers and administrators—an approach similar to parents' visits to mathematics classrooms as outlined in Civil and Menéndez (2012) and Civil and Quintos (2009). Our goals for family members were that they would understand our choice of the reform-based curriculum, air concerns, and better understand how to support their children with mathematics. For teachers, the biggest shift toward fully embracing the student-centered approach to teaching mathematics was in seeing all of their students demonstrate conceptual understanding, think deeply about mathematics, and explain their thinking, all of which were strengthened the longer students were exposed to this approach. We could see students maximizing their learning potential, as stated in the Access and Equity Principle (NCTM 2014). We felt that letting parents see a whole class (which included their own child) engaged in a student-centered mathematics lesson focused on developing conceptual understanding would be the most powerful way to convince them of the approach—much more powerful than anything we could say as instructional leaders.

We began the Open Classroom with an overview of our chosen mathematics curriculum, which included our rationale, alignment to the CCSS, and typical lesson formats. Families were then invited to attend about twenty to thirty minutes of their child's mathematics lesson (all of the mathematics lessons were rescheduled to occur at the same time that day), which included some classes in French or Spanish. Parents were asked to jot down any notes, questions, or concerns they had during the introductory session or classroom observation time so that they could be addressed following the observation. Parents returned to the school library to debrief in small groups by grade level, with the teacher present to answer specific questions about what parents saw or about the grade-level content. Finally, teachers and instructional leaders answered questions from the group as a whole and provided resources for families to learn more about the curriculum, the approach, or mathematics in general. To help parents understand how to best support their children at home, we had prepared some handouts and resources; but in most cases, parents who were present at the meetings offered advice to other parents, as seen in Carolina's testimony in our opening vignette. We noticed that over the years (we are in the fourth year of using the curriculum), more parents have become advocates of an approach based on developing conceptual understanding as they have gained experience with the curriculum.

Content-Based Family Mathematics Sessions

After we implemented our first Open Classroom and based on the feedback from teachers and parents, we realized that some parents were interested in knowing more about how children learn the mathematics specific to the grade level of their child. As a part of our teacher professional development when we transitioned to Investigations, we had explored the Cognitively Guided Instruction (CGI) levels of understanding for problem solving (Carpenter et al. 2014). Part of this professional development for teachers involved videotaping problem-solving interviews with students from our own school in order to understand the levels of understanding for key grade-level skills. We were able to use these resources and teacher leaders to design meetings around how children understand concepts that span a few grade bands, such as addition and subtraction for first and second grade.

We implemented a series of family mathematics sessions with the goal of introducing the idea of multiple strategies for solving problems, the CGI progression of strategies, and curricular strategies for that particular content area. Table 6.1 shows a sample agenda from one of these meetings. Teachers and instructional leadership planned and led these meetings, which included student demonstrations of some of the games from Investigations. Having live demonstrations as well as showing videos of students engaged in the curricular activities proved to be a powerful way for families to understand how a particular activity from the curriculum builds conceptual understanding. We were also able to address parent concerns about key points of contention—such as "learning the times tables," "tricks" for multiplying, and "borrowing"—more specifically in these sessions. For example, in one session we showed a video of a student first using strategies for multiplication that demonstrate conceptual understanding and then trying a "trick" that his uncle had showed him—and the resulting confusion by the student when he came up with two different answers. Parents were able to see that his uncle's method did not allow the student to trace his own thinking and make sense of his answer. These conversations permeated these sessions around content areas; at the same time, we emphasized when it was appropriate to introduce algorithms that parents knew and could share with their children.

Table 6.1. Sample agenda for a family math session

Review Objectives
Learn about multiplication and division in the CCSS and in our curriculum.
Learn how children understand multiplication and division.
Engage in multiplication and division.
Think about how to support your children with multiplication and division.
Progression of Strategies and Problem Types
Curricular Approach to Multiplication and Division
Curriculum in Action

Assessment System and Family Meetings

Finally, we developed a strategy-based problem-solving assessment system that served to solidify teachers' understanding of how to use student thinking to inform their instruction. This in turn allowed us to show students' strategy-use progressions and served as a way to share the importance of promoting conceptual understanding to families. In order to illustrate how we integrated family engagement into our assessment system, I (Georgette) describe the assessment system, how it affected my practice as a teacher, and how I used it with families.

Students are encouraged to show their conceptual understanding when solving mathematical word problems in our school. The use of CGI-based problem-solving interviews as an assessment tool allows students to conceive of and adopt their own strategies for solving problems, rather than memorizing a prescribed algorithm or similar strategies that have no conceptual meaning for the students. During the first trimester of the school year, I selected the mathematics standard of addition and subtraction fluency within 20, in conformity with the CCSS: "Fluently add and subtract within 20 using mental strategies. By the end of grade 2, know from memory all sums of two one-digit numbers" (NGA Center and CCSSO 2010). Students were assessed individually on that skill using a problem-solving-based interview that we drafted and are continually refining. The assessment system was designed to let teachers place a student on a continuum of strategy use aligned with the standards. For example, a student who used a counting strategy for an addition or subtraction problem within 20 would be placed as "approaching" the second-grade standard because the end-of-year expectation for second grade is to use derived facts or a recalled strategy for these problems.

In framing the problem solving with students, I explained that I wanted to get to know how they think about mathematics so I could help them in the classroom. Then I told them that they could solve the problem any way they wanted using the material that I provided (cubes, blank paper and markers). The interview was conversational and semistructured, allowing the students to verbalize their thoughts and the strategies they used to solve several story problems in addition and subtraction. I was pleasantly surprised that the majority of students chose to be tested in French, which is my language of instruction for all subjects (but is almost exclusively the second or third language for my students). The students spend 2.5 days a week in English with my second-grade English co-teacher and 2.5 days a week fully immersed in French with me. There are four types of strategies in the CGI framework: direct modeling, counting, derived facts, and recall or mental strategy.

The goal is for all students to reach or approach the mental strategy levels of recall or derived facts in order to be able to apply these operations to more complex problems. I recorded strategies as students described them or solved the problem, and I verified the accuracy of the answers. Contingent on the strategies used and level of accuracy, the student continued the assessment. I then analyzed the assessment results and determined the strategy primarily used by the student. At the beginning of the year, most of my second graders were using counting strategies for addition and subtraction problems within 20.

Conducting the assessment benefited me not only as a teacher, but also in how I engaged families in supporting their children's mathematics learning. I learned that teaching formal concepts in the target language did not impede students' understanding of numbers and did not create barriers in students' development of conceptual knowledge. Instead, they blossomed academically, learning mathematics with understanding. This experience gave me a singular opportunity to conceive an in-depth picture of students' mathematical thinking and development. The results allowed me to provide instructional techniques and strategies that would help students move to the next strategy level (for example, grouping students strategically to learn from another student, or through targeted mathematics games that encourage moving from one strategy to another). I became familiar with their learning styles and their personal ways of communicating their mathematical thinking, which all contributed to their growth.

During our Academic Parent Teacher Team meetings (APTT; WestEd 2015), which is our format for parent-teacher conferences, I shared with parents their child's word problems assessment for third trimester and also the child's progression of strategy use throughout the three trimesters. First, I explained which standard(s) students were tested on and why the selected standard(s) is (are) paramount to student's grade-level success. Then, in a way that was accessible to families, I explained the four possible strategies that students used to approach addition and subtraction problems during the assessment (see fig. 6.1). I presented an easy-to-understand table of data related to student assessments and provided individual student results on the standard selected in parents' folders, as well as our class average and class goal for the skill. As recommended, I used modeling and questioning to support parents' interpretation of the data, checked for understanding, and invited parents to ask questions.

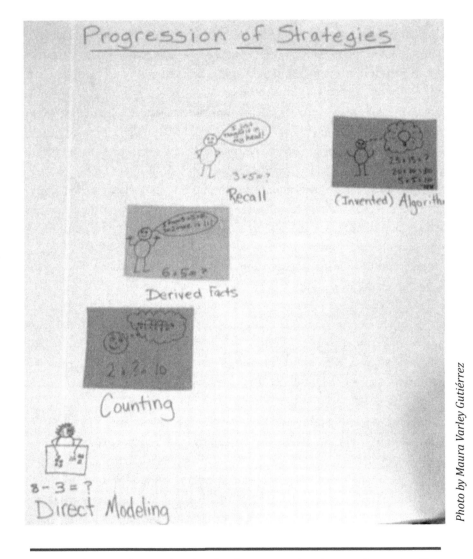

Fig. 6.1. Chart used to explain levels of conceptual understanding to families

I needed to clarify that although the ultimate goal is for students to use efficient and accurate addition and subtraction strategies, it is paramount that they develop number sense and understand numbers, relationships, and operations. I modeled learning activities for families to use in supporting their child's skill development at home; provided guided practice on each learning activity and checked for understanding; and gave parents a chance to practice the take-home activity. Parents were advised to set a reasonable goal for their child's progress for the next trimester.

The second and third APTT meetings followed the same pattern. I assessed students on the same standard(s) that had been selected in the first trimester. Student's accuracy and strategy level were compared to the first trimester results to show individual progress and growth. I invited parents to an APTT meeting to share students' assessment results. In subsequent meetings, parents were more open to ask questions and bring us doubts that they had, because they had a better understanding of the purpose of the meetings and what was required of them and their children. Then we shared the results in terms of class average and growth. Parents had their child's individual growth in their folder, and we displayed the class data in order to provide an overall picture of the class's growth. Of the twenty-three students in the class, all except five moved to the next strategy level over the course of the first trimester.

By the second APTT meeting, parents had realized the importance of supporting their child by practicing the take-home activities and games to help their child reach the class end-of-year goal. All of the parents attended the second meeting. This perfect attendance demonstrated not only parents' interest in the meeting but also their understanding of the benefit of working as a team to support their children's academic success. The third-trimester APTT meeting was rewarding: Twenty out of twenty-three parents replied to the invitation. The results were self-explanatory. All of my students but two moved up at least one level during the third trimester of the school year, in part because of family engagement and collaboration with the teacher. Figure 6.2 is a sample of the kind of easy-to-read data we share at APTT meetings. Each bar represents the distribution of students in the class for each level as described in table 6.2, which is aligned to CCSS. This table was created by our instructional team to be able to place students on a continuum of addition and subtraction fluency aligned to the CCSS. The graph (see fig. 6.2) provides a snapshot of the growth that the class made in the level of strategy used from the first to the third trimester. For example, during the first trimester, 12 percent of students were using counting strategies, derived facts, or recall to solve problems within 20; by the end of the year, 63 percent were using those strategies.

Table 6.2. Levels corresponding to figure 6.2, aligned to student strategies as described in grade-level CCSS

Approaching		Meeting K	
A	B	C	D
Unable to add and subtract within 5 accurately or uses inappropriate strategy.	Add and subtract within 5 using primarily direct modeling or counting strategies.	Add and subtract within 5 using primarily derived facts or recall.	Add and subtract within 10 using primarily direct modeling or counting strategies.

Meeting 1st		Meeting 2nd	
E	F	G	H
Add and subtract within 10 using primarily derived facts or recall.	Add and subtract within 20 using primarily direct modeling.	Fluently add and subtract within 20 using counting strategies or derived facts.	Fluently add within 20 using recall.

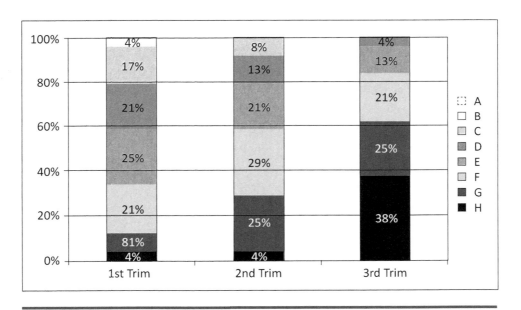

Fig. 6.2. Graph showing a representative distribution of student data organized by percentage of students at each level. (See table 6.2 for description of level correlated with grade-level standards.)

During the first year of these meetings, we found ourselves strongly encouraging parents to explore more concrete strategies when working with their children before emphasizing memorization of basic addition (second graders) and times tables (for our third graders), or teaching the traditional algorithm for multi-digit addition and subtraction. Many parents left unconvinced because other parents at the meetings had validated their feelings. As the years went by, other parents who had testimony from their own children became the primary advocates for not rushing to the most efficient strategy and skipping conceptual understanding.

Carolina, one of Blay's former parents, explained the importance of these family engagement efforts around mathematics: "The key for me is and has been to stay informed. Go to the grade-level meetings. Teachers explain, give examples and tools to work with our kids at home." Parents who attended these events became advocates within the meetings for other parents, explaining the shift in role they had to make in supporting their children, which mirrors the shift teachers must make to teach reform-based mathematics and other student-centered pedagogical approaches. Teachers who shared their assessment data and their experience with the curriculum and students who were observed engaging in student-centered mathematics were advocating for this equitable approach to teaching mathematics. In turn, as parents learned more about the approach over the course of multiple school years, they became natural and convincing advocates for the approach with other parents. Teachers, students, and parents were advocates for reform-based mathematics for all. Ideally, this advocacy is not just on behalf of our own children or within our school but can be used to change the narrative in society of what mathematics instruction should be.

Reflecting and Taking Action

In closing, we offer some of our own current next steps as our work evolves and some words of wisdom for engaging in similar work in other schools or districts from the perspective of a teacher, a parent, and facilitators of family engagement. It is important to consider that our family engagement efforts developed over time and are being revised continually. Named one of the most (racially) diverse schools in Washington, D.C., our school is rapidly shifting in population (we have gone from close to 100 percent of students qualifying for Free and Reduced Lunch ten years ago and 70 percent four years ago to less than 50 percent for the 2016–17 school year) as the city is shifting in population (higher income, whiter) because of gentrification (Chandler 2015). We find that our family engagement efforts need to change along with this shift. For example, Latino families, once a familiar sight in our hallways, are not as present, and we must do more to make sure they feel comfortable and maintain a voice in our school, which is now dominated by more privileged parents. We do reach our Latino families through our APTT meetings and parent-teacher conferences (where teachers share data and activities and invite families to set goals for their children, similar to the APTT meeting content), but we often do not reach many of them through other family engagement efforts. Many of our Latino families have less time off or job flexibility than other families and prioritize the APTT meetings over some other informational meetings such as Open Classroom, and we are planning to explore this situation further. Our next step is to do personal outreach to our Latino families, invite them to provide feedback to give us a sense of their needs, and to shape our family engagement efforts for the coming school years (see chapter 7).

Given our experience, we have two pieces of advice for similar efforts: It is important to grow teacher leaders and to provide space for parent advocacy. Are there teachers who are leading the way with believing in an equitable approach to teaching mathematics? They would be the perfect allies to co-plan and co-facilitate the Open Classrooms and family mathematics sessions. Blay also offers the following words of wisdom that she has learned over the five years she has been hosting the family meetings (APTT meetings):

> It is CRITICAL for the teacher to have a graph that speaks for itself: the clearer the data, the better parents understand it and the greater their cooperation. Also, students' involvement in their parents' invitation is a key to perfect attendance at APTT meetings! We have learned several strategies to increase attendance at these parents meetings over the years. What would a meeting with great charts be worth without parents in attendance? Besides students writing personal invitations to their parents, we do outreach in whatever way that families prefer (text messages, emails, hard copy, etc. . . .) and we provide food and often go into an end-of-trimester learning showcase immediately following the meeting to minimize the days where parents need to request time off. We also offer translation and make-up meetings as needed.

Teachers are on the front lines when it comes to interacting with parents and have the most intimate knowledge of their concerns about mathematics, which can be tapped into. It is important to address those points of contention because they can build mistrust between the school and families or even cause confusion for students.

Do you know of parents within your building who have had a shift in thinking when it comes to mathematics? You could capture their words in a videotaped testimony to use in meetings, or just be sure to give space in the meetings for family testimony. The value of parent testimony is evident in Carolina's own words:

> I want to say to parents: Don't be afraid! This is new, to us anyway. Our kids are learning different strategies and solutions to solve problems. If your concern is that they're not learning the traditional algorithm, I can tell you they will. It's been easier for Adonis to understand algorithms and even better, to be able to solve one problem in about five different ways.

References

Carpenter, Thomas P., Elizabeth Fennema, Megan Loef Franke, Linda Levi, and Susan B. Empson. *Children's Mathematics: Cognitively Guided Instruction*. Portsmouth, N.H.: Heinemann, 2014.

Chandler, Michael Alision. "As D.C. Gentrifies, Some Charter Schools Aim to Reach Broader Spectrum." *Washington Post*, December 4, 2015. https://www.washingtonpost.com/local/education/charter-schools-appealing-to-more-diverse-families-as-dc-gentrifies/2015/12/03/1d79c3f8-8dab-11e5-acff-673ae92ddd2b_story.html?utm_term=.8e4a9fc5ce3b

Civil, Marta, and José María Menéndez. "Parents and Children Come Together: Latino and Latina Parents Speak Up about Mathematics Teaching and Learning." In *Beyond Good Teaching: Advancing Mathematics Education for ELLs*, edited by Sylvia Celedón-Pattichis and Nora Ramirez, pp. 127–38. Reston, Va.: National Council of Teachers of Mathematics, 2012.

Civil, Marta, and Beatriz Quintos. "Latina Mothers' Perceptions about the Teaching and Learning of Mathematics: Implications for Parental Participation." In *Culturally Responsive Mathematics Education*, edited by Brian Greer, Swapna Mukhopadhyay, Sharon Nelson-Barber, and Arthur Powell, pp. 321–43. New York: Routledge, 2009.

D'Addario, Daniel. "Louis C. K. Blasts the Common Core: 'It Feels Like a Dark Time.'" Salon.com. April 29, 2014. http://www.salon.com/2014/04/29/louis_c_k_blasts_the_common_core_it_feels_like_a_dark_time/

Garelick, Barry. "A New Kind of Problem: The Common Core Math Standards." TheAtlantic.com. November 20, 2012. http://www.theatlantic.com/national/archive/2012/11/a-new-kind-of-problem-the-common-core-math-standards/265444/

González, Norma, Luis C. Moll, and Cathy Amanti. *Funds of Knowledge: Theorizing Practice in Households, Communities, and Classrooms*. Mahwah, N.J.: Lawrence Erlbaum Associates, 2005.

Herbel-Eisenmann, Beth, Nathalie Sinclair, Kathryn B. Chval, Douglas H. Clements, Marta Civil, Stephen J. Pape, Michelle Stephan, Jeffery J. Wanko, and Trena L. Wilkerson. "Positioning Mathematics Education Researchers to Influence Storylines." *Journal for Research in Mathematics Education* 47, no. 2 (2016): 102–17.

Legnard, Danielle, and Susan Austin. "The Math Promise: Celebrating at Home and School." *Teaching Children Mathematics* 21, no. 3 (2014): 178–84.

National Council of Teachers of Mathematics (NCTM). *Principles to Actions: Ensuring Mathematical Success for All*. Reston, Va.: NCTM, 2014.

National Governors Association Center for Best Practices and Council of Chief State School Officers (NGA Center and CCSSO). *Common Core State Standards for Mathematics.* Washington, D.C.: NGA Center and CCSSO, 2010. http://wwwcorestandards.org

Nieto, Sonia. *Affirming Diversity: The Sociopolitical Context of Multicultural Education.* Mahwah, N.J.: Erlbaum, 1992.

TERC. *Investigations in Number, Data, and Space.* 2nd ed. Glenview, Ill.: Pearson/Scott Foresman, 2008. http://investigations.terc.edu

WestEd. "Empowering Families to Improve Student Learning." *R&D Alert Online.* December 29, 2015. https://www.wested.org/rd_alert_online/empowering-families-to-improve-student-learning/

CHAPTER 7

Creating Inclusive Opportunities for Family Involvement in Mathematics

Rachel Monette, *University of Georgia*
Amy Noelle Parks, *Michigan State University*

Our orientation toward family involvement began to shift one evening during a prekindergarten mathematics night held at a rural school that served primarily low-income families. The children, with the support of family members and teachers, were making scarecrows from a prepackaged craft kit. The early childhood educators, probably as a result of the progressive pedagogies they had been taught, were quick to tell the children that they could make the scarecrows "any way they wanted," often laying aside the printed directions. In addition, when they intervened to direct the children's attention toward mathematics, it was often to ask the children to count petals or strands of hair or to name the shape of an object, like the triangle-shaped nose or circular eyes. In contrast, the grandfathers, mothers, and aunts helping the children were much more likely to direct the children to look at the written directions, pointing out the way the triangular nose was positioned and encouraging the four-year-olds to use the black-and-white diagram to orient the nose correctly on their own scarecrows. In addition, while the family members

This material is based upon work supported by the National Science Foundation under Grant No. 1461468. Any opinions, findings, and conclusions or recommendations expressed in this material are those of the authors and do not necessarily reflect the views of NSF.

were less likely to ask the children to count, they used mathematical language in order to support the children's efforts to make the scarecrows, such as asking children to get "the long rectangles" or to fold a piece of string in half. They also were much more likely to model using the diagram provided in the directions to solve problems themselves, referring to it to check where a bow should go or which way the triangular hat should point. In doing so, they showed the children how tools such as written diagrams were genuinely useful. When working with family members, in contrast to interacting with educators, children were much more likely to have opportunities to think about moving between two-dimensional and three-dimensional representations of shapes, to think about whether a triangle is still a triangle even when it is oriented in another direction, and to work on problems of transformation as they attempted to match the triangular nose on their scarecrow to the one in the picture. Although the educators' inclination to allow the children to make the scarecrow in whatever way they wanted may have promoted creativity, it did little to create genuine mathematical problems; and while requests for students to count allowed them opportunities to practice an important mathematical skill, often it was not a skill that was authentic in the context of the craft.

We had designed the mathematics night so that families might learn from educators about how to include mathematics during play and other informal activities in their homes. The family members themselves expressed a desire to learn about this, saying things such as, "I never thought about all the math in cooking or in playing." However, after watching family members interact that evening with their children, we became convinced that we needed to do more not only to support family members' engagement with their children around mathematics, but also to allow educators to learn from families. While events like mathematics nights that bring families into school are important, it is also important to provide families with opportunities to engage their children in mathematics at home. Carefully observing families during the mathematics night helped us see that the adults in the children's lives already had many strengths they could use to engage their children in mathematics and that they could do so in productive ways without the supervision of educators. We realized that providing families with mathematics activities to do in their homes would draw on these strengths and allow more families to participate.

Making a Commitment to Access and Equity

Attending to NCTM's Access and Equity Principle requires providing all students with "the support and resources needed to maximize their learning potential" (NCTM 2014, p. 59). Building productive relationships with caregivers and learning about children's lives outside of school are essential to practices for educators who want to respond to this principle. In particular, *Principles to Actions: Ensuring Mathematical Success for All* calls on educators to be "responsive to students' backgrounds, experiences, and knowledge when designing, implementing, and assessing the effectiveness of a mathematics program" (NCTM 2014, p. 60).

Activities designed to promote family involvement, such as the one described in the opening vignette, allow educators to learn more about children and their lives outside of school. When educators see how parents talk to children and hear the stories they tell in informal settings, they can draw on these experiences when engaging with children in the classroom. True responsiveness requires engagement with real children and families. Teachers do not, after all, teach African American, Latin@, white, urban, or rural children *in general*; they teach *particular* children in *particular* places. Without getting to know these individual children and their families, any effort at responsiveness is as likely to be based on cultural stereotypes as on the actual experiences, traditions, or perspectives of the children in any given classroom.

Evenings such as the one described above are one way to build connections between families and school personnel. Learning about how parents engage their children at home is another important way of coming to understand families' cultures and perspectives. As children, family members, and educators engage with one another in playful ways, authentic opportunities occur for learning from one another and for building relationships. These kinds of interactions also open up opportunities for educators to learn, as we did, from families about the productive ways that they engage with their children and to begin to see families as resources and strengths to support mathematical learning. The vignette occurred during a mathematics night at school, but to be truly responsive, educators must think of ways to engage families that do not require that they come into school buildings. Opening up opportunities for engagement is critical to providing access to all families.

In this chapter, we describe some activities designed to build connections between homes and schools, which can be used to inform the kind of responsive pedagogy called for in *Principles to Actions* (NCTM 2014). As part of our desire to honor this principle, we try to replace the word *parents* in our talking and writing with more inclusive vocabulary, such as *family members* or *caregivers*. Because we believe that language plays a critical role in determining who feels included and who feels excluded, we want to use words that communicate to children that all adults in their lives are important and valued and that when we say "family," we mean grandparents, aunts, uncles, and siblings, in addition to parents. The most inclusive language for talking about families is likely to vary from school to school and from classroom to classroom. Being responsive requires that teachers know the adults in the lives of each of their students and that they use the language most likely to include those adults. This commitment, of course, extends beyond building mathematical knowledge and into all efforts to connect homes and schools. Focusing events on particular kinds of family members (e.g., "Grandparents' Day," "Muffins for Moms," etc.) inevitably leads some children to feel excluded. Reframing these days with more inclusive language is a good first step toward building a responsive practice.

Advancing Access and Equity

Family nights, like the one described in the vignette, are very common. Nearly all elementary schools in the United States hold yearly activities to foster family involvement, including open houses, teacher conferences, arts and athletic events, and curriculum nights (Carey et al. 1998). While these types of activities are important, they do require that family members come to the school. For many families, attending evening events presents significant challenges because of work schedules, transportation issues, or child care needs. However, research shows that caring adults who are involved in their children's schooling can improve students' academic achievement (Cheung and Pomerantz 2012; Jeynes 2003), social confidence and behavior (Fantuzzo, Davis, and Ginsburg 1995), and attendance (Epstein and Sheldon 2002). To increase family involvement, educators need to explore ways to build positive relationships with families and to engage caregivers in their children's learning, without always requiring that families come to the school building.

Research behind Take-Home Mathematics Activities

Take-home mathematics activities, such as games, crafts, cooking projects, and storybooks, can be enjoyed by many family members and are more closely connected to practices in which families regularly engage than are traditional homework assignments. When teachers find a way to get feedback from families through these take-home activities, communication opens up between home and school. Teachers can get a glimpse into children's home lives and become more responsive during traditional lessons in school. In addition, activities that can be done at home allow participation by family members who may not be able to attend school-based events because of challenges around transportation, time off work, or access to child care for siblings.

Home-based activities tend to be more common in relation to literacy. For example, to promote early reading, some schools and libraries use family book bags (Dever 2001; Dever and Burts 2002) or backpacks to send home books along with related games and projects. Zeece and Wallace (2009) suggested that using "literacy backpacks" with students involves adults who are "not initially confident or comfortable in an overt role as a child's literacy model[, which] may preclude them from participating in classroom-based activities or formal literacy interventions" (p. 36). Adults who are not fluent readers themselves may be nervous about going to a school event out of fear (justified or not) that they will be embarrassed because they cannot participate in the desired ways (Kyle et al. 2002). Given the high levels of mathematics anxiety in the United States, it is likely that family members may be even more reluctant to participate in public displays of mathematics. Sending home materials allows adults to engage in mathematical activities with their children without worrying about what onlookers might think.

Teachers who can communicate with families by using take-home activities open themselves up to the rich practices that go on in the home, which they may not have known about otherwise. Anderson and Gold (2006) found that many mathematical practices children engaged in at home were not leveraged in school. Take-home activities not only have the potential to provide an alternative way for families to be involved at school but also serve to link the mathematics that goes on at school and in the home. For example, teachers can tell caregivers what they should look for while engaging in take-home activities or make connections between activities and big ideas, such as those described in the Common Core standards (NGA Center and CCSSO 2010). Similarly, family members can send questions and comments back to teachers to help educators develop a greater understanding of children's mathematical thinking.

Take-home activities can provide caregivers with mathematical language to use to scaffold their children's play and can also give children more time to engage in play than they are allowed during busy school days. Recent research suggests that early mathematical play leads to future learning, although there have been far fewer studies of mathematical play in homes than in schools (Wager and Parks 2014). Levine and colleagues (2012) found that children who played with puzzles during observations of their at-home play performed better on a test of spatial skills given months later. Similarly, Ramani and Siegler (2008) found that playing Chutes and Ladders at home correlated with performance on tests of numeracy (unlike play with other kinds of games). In the current school climate, many teachers find that there is less time for play in primary classrooms than ever before. Encouraging play at home through mathematics take-home activities might be a good way to allow students to engage in beneficial play that builds mathematical understanding that otherwise might be hard to fit into the school day. In order to better understand how take-home activities can encourage family involvement and build mathematical understanding through play, we will describe in detail two take-home activities: making and working with modeling dough and building with Lego blocks.

Examples of Play-Based Take-Home Activities

The take-home activities described below were designed as part of a broader research study conducted in a school that served primarily low-income students. For the modeling dough activity, described in figure 7.1, volunteer families were first given a recipe for making the modeling material (similar to Play-Doh), the necessary supplies (including measuring cups and spoons), an audio recorder, and a disposable camera. The written directions asked adults to make the dough with their children and to audio record the process as well as their children's play with the dough afterward. In addition, sets of Lego blocks were sent home to families, along with cameras and audio recorders. (See figure 7.2.)

---

1. Use the recipe below and the ingredients and tools sent home to make a batch of modeling dough (like Play-Doh) with your child. As you cook, talk to your child about the tools you use to measure while cooking and the process of measuring accurately.
2. Allow your child to play with the modeling material for a while. Don't worry about doing anything special. If you like, take pictures of your child's play with a camera and email the pictures to me.
3. Please return the measuring cups and spoons to school in the plastic bag.

Modeling Dough Recipe

Measure into a small pan:

    1 cup flour

    1/2 cup salt

    2 teaspoons cream of tartar

Add:

    1 tablespoon baby oil

    1 cup water with 6 to 10 drops of food coloring added

Cook over medium-high heat. At first it may seem like too much water, but it will boil off and turn solid in about 3 minutes. ALLOW IT TO COOL. Then you and your child can knead it smooth and play!

Fig. 7.1. Making modeling dough

1. Allow your child to play with the blocks freely. You can talk to your child about the creations, asking for descriptions of the structures. You can also point out things you notice about the structures, like when two sides look the same or when different blocks are used to make the same shape.
2. You can also use the provided pictures to encourage your child to make more complex creations. You can help your child think through how to create the structure in real life using the picture.
3. If you like, take pictures and email them to me.

Fig. 7.2. Building with blocks

We used the cameras and recorders to collect data for our research project; however, the activities could easily be done without recording the audio and taking pictures. Alternatively, teachers could invite caregivers to take pictures of children's projects with their cell phones and email them to the teacher. We found that in the rural, low-income community in which we worked, all families had access to at least one cell phone. However, in places where this was not the case, inexpensive digital cameras could be shared over time within the classroom. In addition, teachers may want to check in with some families to see if taking pictures in the home is likely to violate any community norms. In these cases, children could draw pictures of what they did, which would provide similar launch points for discussion in the classroom. Pictures of at-home activities give teachers a chance to share images in class to promote discussion or to launch an in-class activity. For the research project, each child was able to keep the set of Lego blocks sent home; however, backpacks can be used for carrying blocks between home and school. Similarly, the measuring cups and supplies to make the modeling material could be sent home one at a time with students. In order to be inclusive, the necessary materials should be provided through the school. Asking families to buy materials for an at-home project may create a hardship or exclude some students from participating.

In our study, we found that all children who participated in the modeling dough activity at home engaged in counting, typically for an authentic purpose, such as counting the drops of food coloring that needed to go into the material, rather than for a created context such as counting the number of objects made. During play, caregivers and older siblings also used a variety of words related to shape, space, and measurement, including *circle, square, longer, shorter, bigger, cup, half, tablespoon,* and *teaspoon*. This kind of in-the-moment instruction provides a meaningful context in which young children learn mathematical vocabulary as they engage in related experiences. Vocabulary learned in these kinds of authentic contexts is more likely to be supported by rich connections between words, materials, and concepts than vocabulary learned as part of directed instruction at school. For our project, we were interested in documenting the resources family members brought to the activities without much support from educators, but teachers could also send home lists of "mathematics words" related to the activity to jump-start conversations. These activities also offer an opportunity to educate families about the Common Core standards (NGA Center and CCSSO 2010). Currently, there is much confusion around these standards, and helping families understand the language and goals of the standards in the context of activities they enjoy and understand could be quite useful. For example, the kindergarten standards about counting and cardinality call on students to "say the number names in the standard order, pairing each object with one and only one number name and each number name with one and only one object" and to "understand that the last number name said tells the number of objects counted" (p. 1). Sending home a brief discussion of these standards that encourages caregivers to ask their children to point when counting or to repeat the "how many" question after children count a set of objects could help family members come to understand the meaning of the word *cardinality* and could help them develop habits that children can use to build these counting skills.

Teachers can use these activities to share information with families; additionally, teachers can use them to learn how caregivers support or encourage their children. Teachers can ask for either general feedback (e.g., "How did the activity go?") or for specific information they would find useful (e.g., "What did you do when your children got stuck or frustrated?"). Families can respond in person, by email, or through a written note. In our study, we noticed that many mothers made particular efforts to repeat words that may have been unfamiliar to their children. For example, when measuring the oil for the modeling material, Steven's mother said: "Where is the teaspoon? We need one teaspoon of baby oil." And then, apparently after the oil was added, she said, "This is one teaspoon of baby oil." This strategy helped us, and the educators we worked with, to think about how mathematics vocabulary could be introduced in the classroom.

Beyond using mathematical vocabulary, family members also made efforts to teach mathematical concepts to children. Several mothers carefully introduced the measuring cups and spoons to their children, naming each one and asking children to point out which was needed for particular measures. Some mothers also invited their children to think with them about how many scoops would be needed to create two teaspoons or about how to create a variety of shapes with the modeling material. In Elizabeth's case (all names are pseudonyms), she and her five siblings completed the take-home activity together. Her oldest sister led the making of the dough and introduced the measuring cups and spoons as the younger siblings listened and then began participating in the measuring and combining of ingredients. The take-home activity had the power to involve the entire family as they all enjoyed playing with the finished product and making shapes and food items with one another. It also made Elizabeth's teacher think about how her kindergarteners' siblings could be used as resources and about the ways that similar activities could create meaningful contexts for practicing academic oral language, which is critical to both early literacy and mathematics (Kim 2015).

Several caregivers connected making the modeling dough to experiences of cooking and eating food. For example, when starting the activity, Harris's mother said, "You know how Papa watches those chef shows and you see them measure stuff out and they do it like that?" Harris responded: "I'm on a chef show!" Both Harris and his mother returned to this idea while "cooking" the modeling material and playing with it. This context not only connected the mathematical activity to a real-world example (see chapters 1–4) but also gave Harris's mother a way to emphasize the importance of making an exact measurement. The photographs of the modeling dough "food" and the accompanying descriptions that were sent to school provided a window into the family's daily life as well, showing that a cooking show was a context the teacher could draw on in class and expect at least some of the children to understand (see chapter 2). In other families, children were encouraged to create various kinds of food, which opened up opportunities for children to engage in visualization and geometric reasoning while they kept the image of the food in their minds and then made a three-dimensional representation of it with the modeling dough. For example, in response to his mother's prompts about food, Steven created french fries, a hamburger, a hot dog, and a cookie. The pictures and the student's verbal description of them (see example in fig. 7.3) provided the teacher with some access to thinking about the kinds of foods that were common in children's homes.

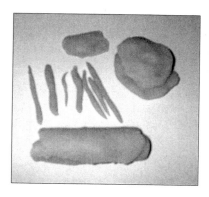

Fig. 7.3. Steven made a hot dog, french fries, and a cookie

As with the modeling dough activity, the Lego blocks presented various opportunities for mathematical engagements in children's homes. In particular, the invitation to build structures encouraged children to engage in a variety of composing and decomposing activities. Along with the blocks, teachers could send information about composing and decomposing, concepts that are addressed repeatedly in the primary grade Common Core mathematics standards. Kindergarteners are asked in the geometry standards to "compose simple shapes to form larger shapes" (NGA Center and CCSSO 2010, p. 1). Describing these standards in relation to building with Lego blocks provides a way of helping families make sense of this mathematical language and can also point adults toward the important mathematics in this activity, suggesting that families ask questions such as "Can you go all the way around to make a square?" or "How many short rectangles do you need to make a long one?"

The kits we sent home also had pictures of structures that could be made from the blocks. Much of the students' play with the blocks focused on making the structures shown in the pictures, often supported by comments from adults and older siblings. As in the vignette that opened this chapter, caregivers directed their children to attend to the pictures and helped them make sense of how to translate the two-dimensional representation into a three-dimensional structure. The children, guided by adults in their families, engaged in visualization and geometric reasoning. During interviews after the study, family members were often pleased to hear that the support they offered their children (such as reminding them to look at the diagrams) helped the children's mathematical thinking. One mother said, "I didn't think I was good at math," which demonstrates that competently engaging in activities such as this one can help caregivers reframe themselves as able to support their children's mathematical learning.

As with the modeling dough activity, family members used a variety of words during the creation of the structures related to shape and space, including *square*, *circle*, *rectangle*, *longer*, *shorter*, *bigger*, and *smaller*. As the caregivers and the children searched for specific pieces among all the blocks in the bucket, many adults chose to repeat the color, shape, and size of the piece they were searching for. Once the child thought he had found the matching piece, it would be compared to the piece in the picture and then there would be a determination of how many of those pieces were necessary to complete the structure. For example, Laura decided that she wanted to make a house that she saw on one of the picture cards. The structure required several types of different pieces. As Laura gathered the pieces, her mother joined in the search to make sure that all the necessary pieces were located. Her mother said, "We need a door, we need one of . . . yep, and one of those . . . here . . . one here . . . the one that is green." The guidance most often focused on the number of each of the blocks needed to complete the structure. Students might need four tire pieces to make their car or five flower pots to match the picture on the card. Searching for the needed blocks not only engaged children in counting and mathematical vocabulary but also helped them begin to recognize the relationships between parts and wholes. Pictures taken by family members showed that some children used their own pieces to create variations on the pictures on the cards. For example, Lyla placed flowers on the top of the barn structure she built looking at the card (as shown in fig. 7.4), and Taylor found alternative blocks to compose a rectangular prism that was part of the pictured car he was building.

Fig. 7.4. Lyla makes a decorated barn

Reflecting and Taking Action

Although our project focused on Lego blocks and modeling dough, a variety of options exists for creating engaging mathematical take-home activities. For example, a set of puzzles could be sent home to families to reinforce concepts of composing and decomposing, orientation of shapes, and spatial skills. Puzzle play has been shown to pay off for students in later tests of spatial ability (Levine et al. 2012). Teachers can also send home commercial games, such as Hi-Ho! Cherry-O or dominoes, for children to play. As mentioned earlier in the chapter, games can improve students' numeracy skills. Simple card games could also serve as engaging play-based take-home activities. Cards with numerals, dots, tally marks, or other representations can be sent home in a bag with directions on how to play a game commonly called War or Compare. To play, students split the cards evenly with an adult or sibling, with each person putting his cards facedown in a pile in front of him. Players flip over the card at the top of their deck at the same time, and the person with the greater-value card takes both. The game continues until all cards have been played against one another. Whoever has the most cards at the end of the game wins. Similarly, supplies for art projects, such as glue sticks and small objects like toothpicks or sequins, can be sent home with suggestions that children make a variety of pictures each with the same number of objects. Activities like these develop students' number recognition, sense of quantity, and one-to-one correspondence. These skills are foundational to later work involving place value and operations; however, many curricula do not allot sufficient time for children to solidify these skills in the classroom. Take-home activities not only provide children with additional opportunities for practice but also give caregivers a chance to observe their children's counting skills. In addition, these kinds of activities allow children to engage with mathematics in settings where they feel competent and allow families to adjust what they are doing in response to their culture and ways of interacting with each other. These kinds of interactions help break down barriers between school and home. Teachers can promote and take advantage of observations at home by taking time during conferences to ask adults about what they have observed during these activities at home, instead of using the time only to provide information about what children do at school. These kinds of conversations can help teachers understand the resources available to children, which could be mobilized in planning mathematics lessons, as called for in the Access and Equity Principle, by allowing teachers to better understand their children's backgrounds, cultures, and home experiences (see chapters 8 and 10).

It is important to remember that play-based take-home activities do not have to be complicated to achieve the goals of involving families in schooling and engaging students with mathematical concepts in fun and creative ways. In developing these activities, teachers might ask themselves: What materials do I have access to that could be used in mathematical engagements at home? What kinds of games or experiences do I hear my children talking about that could be built on to elicit mathematics? What activities or projects are described in my curriculum that might be well suited to doing at home?

Educating families about where mathematics can be found in early play helps teachers form a connection between home and classroom activities and empowers caregivers to engage with their children around mathematics at home. This type of activity also creates opportunities for teachers to learn from families about both their home life and their children's mathematical thinking while allowing families who may not be able to attend evening events in schools to be more closely connected to their children's school experiences.

References

Anderson, Diane D., and Eva Gold. "Home to School: Numeracy Practices and Mathematical Identities." *Mathematical Thinking and Learning* 8, no. 3 (2006): 261–86.

Carey, Nancy, Laurie Lewis, Elizabeth Farris, and Shelley K. Burns. *Parent Involvement in Children's Education: Efforts by Public Elementary Schools* (NCES 98-032). Washington, D.C.: U.S. Government Printing Office, 1998.

Cheung, Cecilia S., and Eva M. Pomerantz. "Why Does Parents' Involvement Enhance Children's Achievement? The Role of Parent-Oriented Motivation." *Journal of Educational Psychology* 104, no. 3 (2012): 820–32.

Dever, Martha T. "Issues in Education: Family Literacy Bags: A Vehicle for Parent Involvement and Education." *Journal of Early Education & Family Review* 8, no. 4 (2001): 17–28.

Dever, Martha T., and Diane C. Burts. "An Evaluation of Family Literacy Bags as a Vehicle for Parent Involvement." *Early Child Development and Care* 172, no. 4 (2002): 359–70.

Epstein, Joyce L., and Steven B. Sheldon. "Present and Accounted for: Improving Student Attendance through Family and Community Involvement." *Journal of Educational Research* 95, no. 5 (2002): 308–18.

Fantuzzo, John W., Gwendolyn Y. Davis, and Marika D. Ginsburg. "Effects of Parent Involvement in Isolation or in Combination with Peer Tutoring on Student Self-Concept and Mathematics Achievement." *Journal of Educational Psychology* 87, no. 2 (1995): 272–81.

Jeynes, William H. "A Meta-Analysis: The Effects of Parental Involvement on Minority Children's Academic Achievement." *Education and Urban Society* 35, no. 2 (2003): 202–18.

Kim, Young-Suk. "Language and Cognitive Predictors of Text Comprehension: Evidence from Multivariate Analysis." *Child Development* 86, no. 1 (2015): 128–44.

Kyle, Diane W., Ellen McIntyre, Karen B. Miller, and Gayle H. Moore. *Reaching Out: A K–8 Resource for Connecting Families and Schools.* Thousand Oaks, Calif.: Corwin, 2002.

Levine, Susan C., Kristin R. Ratliff, Janellen Huttenlocher, and Joanna Cannon. "Early Puzzle Play: A Predictor of Preschoolers' Spatial Transformation Skill." *Developmental Psychology* 48, no. 2 (2012): 530.

National Council of Teachers of Mathematics. (NCTM). *Principles to Actions: Ensuring Mathematical Success for All.* Reston, Va.: NCTM, 2014.

National Governors Association Center for Best Practices and Council of Chief State School Officers (NGA Center and CCSSO). *Common Core State Standards for Mathematics.* Washington, D.C.: NGA Center and CCSSO, 2010. http://www.corestandards.org

Ramani, Geetha B., and Robert S. Siegler. "Promoting Broad and Stable Improvements in Low-Income Children's Numerical Knowledge through Playing Number Board Games." *Child Development* 79, no. 2 (2008): 375–94.

Wager, Anita A., and Amy N. Parks. "Learning Mathematics through Play." In *Handbook of Play and Learning in Early Childhood*, edited by Elizabeth Brooker, Mindy Blaise, and Susan Edwards, pp. 216–27. London: Sage, 2014.

Zeece, Pauline D., and Betty M. Wallace. "Books and Good Stuff: A Strategy for Building School to Home Literacy Connections." *Early Childhood Education Journal* 37, no. 1 (2009): 35–42.

CHAPTER 8

Using the Mathematics They Know and Maximizing the Mathematics They Don't: Making Contexts Work

Edd V. Taylor, *University of Colorado, Boulder*

As part of a year-long professional development program focused on creating lessons and developing teaching strategies that support connections between everyday mathematics knowledge and classroom mathematics, a small group of K–grade 2 teachers described the difficulty their students had in solving the mathematics in the lessons they created. Teachers began by reporting, to their grade-level groups, the success they experienced with lessons created during the previous session. Each teacher also described the difficulty students had during their first lesson and how they were more successful with subsequent lessons. As the discussion continued, the teachers began to agree that the students had difficulty with their initial lessons because of the way in which these lessons used the context of students' lives. The mathematics that students were asked to use in solving problems in teachers' initial lessons was quite different from the mathematics students typically used in these contexts. Ms. Cole (names and locations in this chapter are pseudonyms) remarked that her lessons followed this pattern. In her lesson, which

This research was supported in part by a grant from the National Science Foundation (ESI9911679). The opinions, findings, and recommendations expressed in this paper do not necessarily reflect the position, policy, or endorsement of the NSF.

involved setting a table, she asked students to determine how many items were needed for one place setting. The students agreed that the answer was 5. Then, she said, "I wondered how we could figure out how many items were needed for two people." She asked her students how many items would be needed for three people, hoping they might consider counting by fives. She then reflected that she began to see a mismatch in the ways she wanted students to engage in the mathematics (counting by multiples of 5) and the ways they actually used mathematics to solve the problem at home (counting individual items; see fig. 8.1).

How many items are used to make one place setting? [5]

How many items are used to make place settings for two people? [10]

What about for three people? [15]

Fig. 8.1. How many items for place settings?

Noticing this mismatch, Ms. Cole reflected:

> Well, the first time [I created lessons] on setting the table, but then decided that it was just the context that the kids were actually thinking about, you know, how many forks or how many spoons? So it was more using the context of what they do, rather than the math that they use at home.

She further explained how children who set the table would grab the number of each utensil (forks, knives, and spoons) to match the number of people eating, but rarely tried to determine the total number of utensils needed, which was the goal of the lesson. In the revised lesson, she used a situation in which the mathematics that the students used in their out-of-school context was more similar to what was asked for in the lesson: "So this time . . . I did stuff about counting money to go to the store, and then getting change back. How much change would you get back?"

Making a Commitment to Access and Equity

Why is it that a first grader who counts on her fingers when doing single-digit addition in her mathematics class can quickly add and subtract numbers in her head while playing games with her friends? How do we take advantage of the mathematics students learn outside of school? The Access and Equity Principle in *Principles to*

Actions: Ensuring Mathematical Success for All (NCTM 2014) describes the need to "leverag[e] students' culture, conditions, and language to support and enhance mathematics learning" (p. 63). Making a commitment to build on what students bring to the classroom becomes an important means to address access and equity. Yet, as the vignette highlights, many teachers find it difficult to connect to students' mathematics learning, and children who have rich mathematical understandings outside the classroom sometimes struggle to solve basic mathematics problems in classrooms.

Advancing Access and Equity

In order to advance access and equity, teachers need to "know and understand the cultures and communities from which their students come and ... also use this knowledge to create meaningful tasks that build on students' prior knowledge and experiences" (NCTM 2014, p. 69). In this chapter, I describe two frameworks that may be useful in understanding different types of mathematical links between in-school and out-of-school mathematics and how they might be used to leverage students' everyday knowledge to support access and equity. The Math Engagement Framework can help teachers expand the ways in which they link lessons to students' everyday knowledge, and the Word-problem Expansive Framework can help teachers choose from multiple purposes in creating the context of word problems. Students participate in activities involving mathematics in ways that differ greatly; these frameworks support teachers in considering their particular students' everyday mathematics knowledge. The two frameworks were designed through collaborations with teachers taking part in a yearlong professional development workshop and through feedback from preservice teachers enrolled in an elementary mathematics pedagogy course.

Math Engagement Framework

The Math Engagement Framework (MEF) consists of two dimensions teachers might consider when constructing pedagogical strategies and creating lessons. The first dimension, _personal relevance_, considers the degree (high to low/never) to which children are participating in a particular activity outside the classroom. The second dimension, _embeddedness_, represents the degree to which mathematics is embedded in a particular activity. While some activities naturally involve mathematics or require mathematics in order to participate (highly embedded mathematics), others require teachers to "add" mathematics to the activity when mathematics might not be central to participation (low embeddedness).

Using the MEF (see fig. 8.2), teachers can consider the dimensions of personal relevance and embeddedness together and along a continuum for each dimension. These dimensions allow for a variety of activities, including those in which mathematics is highly embedded but less personally relevant, as well as those that are highly relevant activities but in which mathematics is not embedded. Ms. Cole's initial lesson, for example, is represented in quadrant II. She focused on the highly relevant activity of setting the table, but the mathematics she asked students to use was quite different from the mathematics they would normally use in that activity. While some teachers may have already considered strategies to link in- and out-of-school practices, this framework is useful in expanding the types of strategies teachers might consider. Another teacher might focus on highlighting the mathematics that children used in their everyday lives (quadrant I), where mathematics is embedded in a highly relevant activity. Others might ask students to participate in a new activity that includes embedded mathematics (quadrant IV). For example, even though students would not usually make a list of items needed for a camping trip, determining the number of items needed is embedded mathematics within a less personally relevant activity.

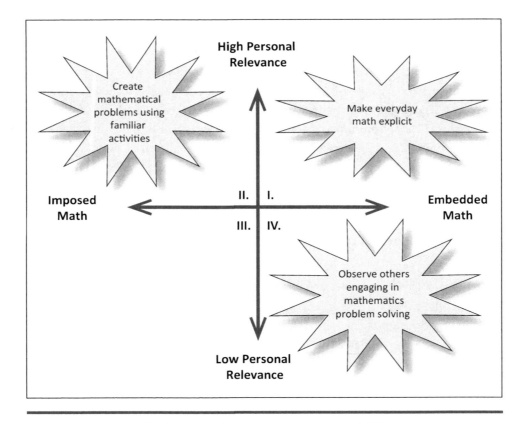

Fig. 8.2. Math Engagement Framework (MEF)

Strategies for Creating Lessons Using the MEF

The suggestions that follow consider differences in levels of personal relevance and mathematical embeddedness and fit nicely in the different quadrants of this framework, highlighting various combinations of embeddedness and personal reference.

Suggestion 1: Make explicit for students the mathematics of their everyday lives. Whether computing totals in candy store purchases or calculating sums of sports teams' scores, children engage in a number of activities that involve mathematics when they are outside of the classroom (Brenner 1998; Nasir 2000). The types of activities are as varied as the mathematics competencies that they develop.

One common challenge to building on students' everyday knowledge, as reported by teachers during professional development workshops, is in focusing on the mathematics embedded in children's activities. As Ms. Cole discovered, drawing on students' everyday situations can be a powerful way to convey certain mathematical problems, but it is not the same as actually drawing on the mathematics they use outside of school. An example of this difference can be explained within the context of sports. Teachers created tasks that described quite accurately the context of a football game. One teacher's initial mathematics task involved the important role of supporters in the stands. Students were told the number of benches at the stadium and the number of supporters on each bench, then were asked to determine the total number of fans in the stadium (see fig. 8.3).

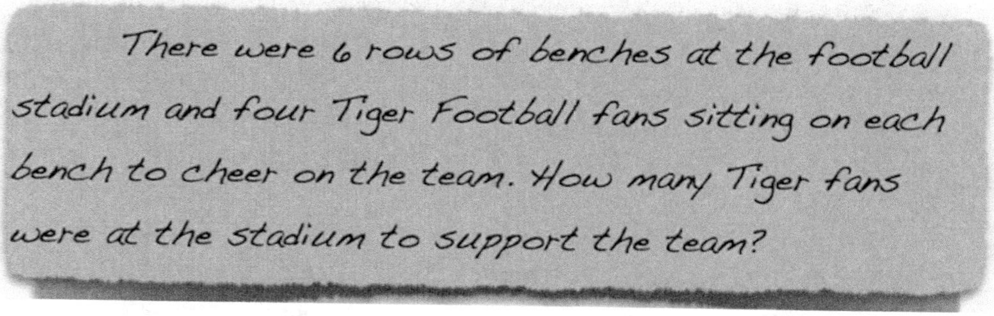

> There were 6 rows of benches at the football stadium and four Tiger Football fans sitting on each bench to cheer on the team. How many Tiger fans were at the stadium to support the team?

Fig. 8.3. Number of fans at the stadium

While this was an interesting way to draw students into an addition problem, the teacher later noted that her word problem was not drawing on the mathematics students actually use in that context. In relation to the two MEP dimensions, the football stadium context is highly relevant, but the mathematics used was not embedded in the activity; rather, it was added by the teacher.

To make the mathematics in this activity both relevant and embedded, one teacher suggested considering how, in football, students are commonly thinking about multiples of 3, 6, and 7 (that is, the number of points for a field goal, a touchdown, and a touchdown with an extra point, respectively). Students can calculate differences to determine the number of points that are needed to tie or win the game, or they can reason about the combinations of numbers that make up a sum and try to determine what combination of scoring methods could result in a particular sum (or score). Much of the same rich reasoning about numbers we value in classrooms can be observed as students problem solve in the context of sports.

Activities involving children's use of money are also popular examples of highly relevant activities with embedded mathematics. Children use money every day: to buy small snacks or a toy, to determine how much money they would have left after a transaction to purchase more items. While many of these store or purchasing problems can be solved using standard classroom methods, children often use sophisticated invented strategies that may highlight important mathematical understanding, including repeated addition to find the totals of multiple candies or even estimation during purchasing. In a study related to children's mathematics in small corner stores, first- and second-grade students used estimation, arithmetic, and operations with rational numbers during a variety of purchasing tasks (Taylor 2009).

Suggestion 2: Add mathematics, or "mathematize," students' everyday activities. What happens when children are not using mathematics that is embedded in practices, but you want to ensure that the mathematics in which they are engaged is still personally relevant? While drawing on embedded mathematical knowledge is often overlooked when considering out-of-school knowledge, there are still useful ways to draw on students' experiences using context alone. Teachers can use examples and activities from students' everyday lives and help their students see how mathematics might be used in these activities (LópezLeiva, Torres, and Khisty 2013).

Recall Ms. Cole's initial lesson about setting a table. The child considers that each setting needs a fork (or two), a spoon, and a knife. The mathematics involved in determining the number of specific utensils, as well as the total number of utensils, needed for n number of family members may seem embedded in the activity, but the activity actually is mathematized. While the context may be common for some children, they rarely use addition or multiplication to determine the appropriate number of utensils; instead, most children grab "enough" of each utensil and put them on the table until all places are covered. Although this type of activity may be ripe for mathematical problem solving and may be quite "real" for students, it is important to remember that the types of mathematical problems students are asked to solve might be totally new.

Choosing a mathematizing strategy offers some clear benefits. First, it provides teachers flexibility in choosing the mathematics they would like to support. For example, if a teacher is providing Join Change Unknown problem types, he can choose to mathematize a student's everyday activity that matches the mathematics of the classroom (see fig. 8.4).

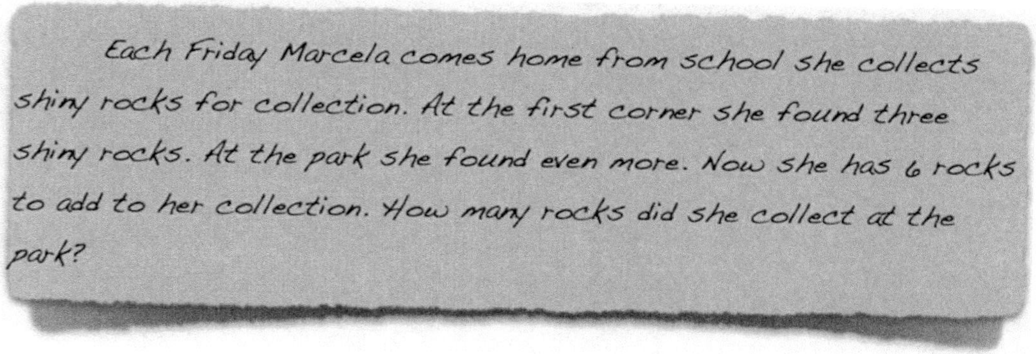

Each Friday Marcela comes home from school she collects shiny rocks for collection. At the first corner she found three shiny rocks. At the park she found even more. Now she has 6 rocks to add to her collection. How many rocks did she collect at the park?

Fig. 8.4. Mathematizing everyday activity

Second, mathematizing helps reinforce the utility of mathematics in connecting it to a personally relevant activity. Third, it may help students think of themselves, and not just others, as "doers" of mathematics. Finally, mathematizing may help students see that mathematics is all around them.

In an effort to use a personally relevant activity with mathematics embedded, Ms. Cole created a store within her classroom. She chose items and prices that matched the mathematics she wanted to highlight that day and that were familiar to students. Adding the mathematics to the familiar/relevant context for students allowed her greater flexibility in linking her students' everyday experiences to the mathematics goals within her classroom.

Suggestion 3: Observe others who are engaged in mathematics activities.
A third way to make use of everyday mathematics is to consider the embedded mathematics of activities in which students do not participate. Drawing on personally relevant activities can be fruitful, but it is also useful to observe the mathematics used by others. What mathematics is the custodian using to draw the Four Square lines on the playground? What method of problem solving is the cashier using in the cafeteria? Observing these activities as a class (or asking students to observe individually) may make it more likely that students will consider the mathematics all around them and perhaps the utility of mathematics outside of school.

Word-problem Expansive Framework

> **Reflective activity.** Consider your current or future classroom. Create word problems that can represent 7 + 3 = 10 and another that can represent 8 + 14 = 22. Now, consider the contexts you wrote for these problems. How might you describe the contexts of the two problems you created?

While teachers commonly consider the mathematical goals of word problems, the nonmathematical goals of these contexts are rarely addressed. Not every word problem must have a stated goal (other than the mathematical content); but students will read a countless number of word problems throughout their years of schooling, so we should be strategic about the contexts we choose for these problems. Consider, for example, the ways some teachers, schools, and districts examine textbooks for their illustrations to ensure that they represent diversity (e.g., race, culture, gender, interests, physical abilities). Similarly, we should think about the topics and "characters" in our word problems and the possible messages sent by these choices. In analyzing the word problems that teachers created during our PD and preservice sessions, we found that more than half were about food, about one quarter about work and play, and another quarter about classroom social situations. How might we take advantage of the flexibility we have in writing word problems to support equitable learning in the classroom, build classroom community, and draw from students' everyday knowledge?

Avoiding Similarity Bias

Another way to address access and equity is by "acknowledging student contributions, and attending to culture and language" (NCTM 2014, p. 65). In addition to expanding the types of problem contexts we consider writing, the framework also allows us to reduce our own context biases; that is, we can sometimes forget how the contexts we use may be related to our own understandings and experiences in the world, thus privileging students who have experiences similar to our own and disadvantaging others.

Consider the example of a word problem written and shared by a preservice teacher in a mathematics pedagogy class:

> There were 3 snow hills on the playground. An hour later it began to snow. After the snow stopped, the custodian plowed the playground. Now there are 5 snow hills. How many new snow hills did the custodian make?

When I heard this problem, I was quite confused. I had thought the teacher was going to create a Join Change Unknown problem in the format 3 + __ = 5. But I was having difficulties understanding how there were more snow hills *after* the custodian plowed them. I wondered if she was creating a subtraction (difference) problem. My limited experience with snow, at that point in my life, made understanding the structure of the mathematics difficult and created a great teachable moment in regard to similarity bias. What was assumed to be common knowledge, that plowing creates hills from the build-up of the removed snow, was just not something I had ever thought about, having grown up in California. "Why would there be more snow hills if he just plowed?" I wondered. It was a rich example of how shared life experiences between students and teacher can further serve to privilege the learning of some students and disadvantage those who do not have those experiences (e.g., recent immigrants from warmer climates), and it is consistent with the ways in which the Access and Equity Principle highlights the need to understand the community in which your students live.

Others have noted similar differences in teacher and student knowledge. Ladson-Billings (1995) described how a task that asked students to determine the potential cost savings from buying a bus pass to get to and from work was based on assumptions that parents only worked one job. By being purposeful in the creation of word problems, we do not need to leave students unexposed to new customs, ideas, and objects. Rather, we can more easily address some similarity biases and also provide students with opportunities to learn about things beyond their current knowledge.

Descriptions of the WEF Seven Purposes

The Word-problem Expansive Framework (WEF) can be used to expand the type of word problems teachers create. The framework comprises these seven purposes: student interest; curricular integration; multicultural; inclusion; get to know you; funds of knowledge; and social justice (see table 8.1). I will provide a brief overview of the first three purposes, since they are likely quite familiar, and more detailed descriptions of the final four purposes.

Student interest. One of the purposes discussed most often in the literature is creating word problems to increase student interest, that is, including topics, items, and activities that keep students engaged. Research in this area has included examining strategies such as placing the names of students in the problem and changing the context of a textbook word problem to reflect a particular student's interest. Evidence indicates that students using personalized word problems are more likely to try to make sense of the problems that match their interest, but students can also find it more difficult to solve word problems using activities that do not match their interest (Renninger, Ewen, and Lasher 2002; Turner et al. 2009). Writing problems that connect to students' interests is a common and important purpose for creating this type of problem.

Curricular integration. Teachers have also used word problems to support curricular integration. Successful strategies include developing mathematics word problems that can be answered directly by drawing on information in a story read during language arts or creating project-based mathematics lessons with themes linked to topics in social studies, language arts, or science. Other strategies teachers have used include graphing or measuring information found in other content areas, e.g., graphing the number of months ripped from Toad's calendar in the book *Frog and Toad Are Friends* (Lobel 1970) or creating project-based lessons related to a particular story.

Multicultural. Another familiar purpose for word problems is to teach about or celebrate various cultures, often by drawing on particular holidays (e.g., Cinco de Mayo, St. Patrick's Day, Martin Luther King Jr. Day). These types of word problems can support teaching not only about more surface-level cultural knowledge (e.g., food) but also about deeper cultural knowledge, histories, and beliefs. While it is more common to see these problems during special holidays, I argue that they should be a regular part of a teacher's presentation of word problems.

Inclusion. More than simply exposing students to the diversity of their peers' experiences, *inclusion* also means building a climate in the classroom that includes historically marginalized individuals and groups. Word problems of this type are particularly powerful when they are not given dramatic fanfare but are presented alongside problem contexts that are more typically represented in classrooms. Despite the fact that only 46 percent of children live in homes that would be considered a traditional family (Livingston 2014), we often see word problems that present a traditional family structure. For students in homes with stepparents, single parents, and same-gender parents, constantly hearing word problems of this type can further marginalize their families and also make these real-world problems less real. Instead, a word problem might be created that includes Gotcha Day, the term for the day on which parents meet their adoptive child for the first time. While the temptation might be to provide elaborate explanations about adoption (and there can be important reasons to do this), discussing a Gotcha Day without the greater class discussion highlights how families formed through adoption are just another type of family. Students who are differently abled or who have different immigration histories or language backgrounds are also ripe topics for inclusion problems.

> **Inclusion example.** Kehla and her entire family are celebrating the day she was adopted. To celebrate, her brother brought 2 cupcakes to her party, and her sister brought 3 more cupcakes. How many cupcakes did they have all together for the party?

Get to know you. As students learn more about their classmates, word problems can be an opportunity to support group work, classroom community, trust, and risk taking. So while talking about a student receiving a porcelain doll at her older sister's *quinceañera* could serve a multicultural purpose, a word problem about a particular student's role in the celebration is an opportunity for students to learn more about their classmate. This purpose for the word problems is particularly useful at the start of the year, as well as for new students throughout the year.

Funds of knowledge. The term *funds of knowledge* has been used to describe strategies to build on the mathematics knowledge children develop in their everyday lives (González et al. 2001). Recall the distinction made in the first section between mathematized tasks and authentic tasks in which mathematics is embedded. A funds-of-knowledge word problem should represent high personal relevance and high embeddedness—mathematics is embedded in an activity in which students already participate. A distinction should be made between the funds-of-knowledge purpose and the student-interest purpose: that is, the mathematics in student-interest problems does not need to be similar to mathematics they might use in their activity of interest.

While a student may have an interest in camping, a mathematized word problem about determining the total number of tents within a camping area is unlikely to use the mathematics that students actually use when camping. In contrast, a student who helps with snacks during outdoor cooking may regularly consider number patterns related to the number and order of graham crackers, chocolate, and marshmallows.

> **Funds of knowledge example.** Think about when you made s'mores while camping at Yosemite. Use the brown, beige, and white colored chips to show the correct pattern of marshmallow, chocolate, and graham cracker for the perfect s'more.

The mathematics used to solve this example is similar to what students might use in that context and contrasts with the student-interest version where the mathematics used is quite different.

Social justice. An increasing number of teachers have chosen to support their students in using mathematics to see and address issues of injustice. The discussion of teaching mathematics for social justice is worthy of its own exploration, and others have written about ways to incorporate mathematics for social justice in their classrooms (see Wager and Stinson 2012). After developing ways to incorporate mathematics for social justice, teachers can also include these topics in word problems.

In the early elementary grades, these topics can be related not only to inequities that students see around them but also to developing knowledge and dispositions to address inequities. For example, in first grade, a word problem might address differences in the availability of sports teams for girls as compared to those for boys. They might also address issues of homelessness, hunger, race, and discrimination based on ability. Although it is beyond the scope of this chapter to deeply investigate approaches to teaching mathematics for social justice, it remains an important component of the WEP model that describes multiple purposes of word problems.

Table 8.1. Word-problem Expansive Framework descriptions and examples

Purpose	Description	Example
Student interest	Math is linked to students' interest to support engagement.	María scored two goals during soccer for four weeks in a row. How many goals has she made so far?
Curricular integration	Provides students opportunity to make links between math content and other content areas.	Toad wants to sleep for 12 months. He has already slept 8 months. How many more months will he want to sleep?
Multicultural	To provide opportunities for students to learn about other cultures.	Jiang received 4 red envelopes from his family members for Chinese New Year. Each envelope had 4 Sacagawea coins. How many coins did he receive from his family this year?
Inclusion	Creates inclusion for groups traditionally marginalized.	Shavon needs to replace the wheels on her wheelchair every 24 months. If 8 months have passed, how many more months will she have before replacing her tires?
Get to know you	Provides opportunity for students to learn more about each as a way to support classroom community.	Amir is enjoying his favorite pastime of cooking while listening to his favorite Ke$ha album. In making khoresh (a Persian stew), he knows that he will need 2 cups of rice for friends he is serving. There are now 6 cups of rice in the kitchen. How many friends can he serve at dinner?
Funds of knowledge	Math is linked to students' mathematical knowledge developed outside of school.	It is the last quarter of the football game and the Wildcats are losing to the Buffalos by a score of 10–7. How many points do the Wildcats need to score in order to tie the game?
Social justice	Math is used to help students recognize injustice in the world.	Morey Elementary School has eight sports teams for boys, and five for girls. How many more sports can the boys play after school as compared to the girls?

Reflecting and Taking Action

The first step in trying to build on students' everyday mathematics knowledge is to know your students and their community. It is difficult to make links to children's lives if you are not sure what their everyday lives are like. Below are some great first steps in this process.

Use Activity Questionnaires

Develop a questionnaire to discover the types of activities in which your students participate. Perhaps students help in their parents' family business or discuss sports scores with their grandparents. In designing this questionnaire, consider open-ended questions that allow parents to list a variety of activities in which their children participate. In addition, a good survey should also encompass the many types of mathematical activities that parents might not consider on their own (like converting recipes when cooking or even discussing the shapes of signs during car games during road trips). After collecting the surveys, try to consider the types of activities that involve groups of students or a large number of students. During the PD described in the vignette, surveys collected by teachers revealed that almost all students were involved in athletics and that there were no gender differences in the level of sports participation. Figure 8.5 highlights the questionnaire developed by teachers in one PD program. It includes open-ended and multiple choice questions.

Similarly, short questionnaires were made in my preservice classes so teachers could better learn about their students and eventually create inclusion, multicultural, and get-to-know-you word problems. In contrast to the activity survey, these items focused on students' favorites (e.g., food, shows, musicians) and topics such as birth order (oldest, youngest, middle), places they have traveled, family traditions, and surprising facts about themselves.

Take Advantage of Parent Teacher Conferences

In addition to showing parents that you are interested in their child, asking parents about their child's participation in activities after school can provide you with a wealth of information about students' opportunities to engage in personally relevant mathematics. Keep a list of these activities handy so that you might personalize mathematics connections during class periods.

Name:_____

Date: _____

Math Outside of School - Part 1

At last, some homework for your parents to do!!! Please have a parent or guardian discuss and answer the following questions with you.

1. What is/was your occupation?
   a. Parent/guardian _____
   b. Parent/guardian _____

2. How is math involved in your day-to-day work?
   _____
   _____

3. Is your child involved in your work (e.g., selling at the farmers market, helping out at your business)?
   a. Parent/guardian _____
   c. Parent/guardian _____

4. What hobbies/interests does your family have?
   _____
   _____

5. How is math involved in your hobbies?
   _____
   _____

6. In what ways do you use math at home with your child?
   _____
   _____
   _____

7. How do you see your child using math outside of school?
   _____
   _____
   _____

Fig. 8.5. Sample questionnaire

Name:_____

Date: _____

Math Outside of School - Part 2

Today you have some homework for your parents to do!!! Please have a parent or guardian discuss and answer the following questions with you. Please check off any of the following activities in which your child participates (this is a multi-grade survey so some activities may not apply):

Games:
- ☐ Monopoly
- ☐ Yahtzee
- ☐ Cards
- ☐ You-Gi-oh
- ☐ _____
- ☐ _____

Cooking:
- ☐ Measuring ingredients
- ☐ Determining time things will be ready
- ☐ Setting the table
- ☐ _____

Money:
- ☐ Allowance
- ☐ Giving money
- ☐ Spending on their own
- ☐ Calculating the tip at restaurants
- ☐ _____

Transportation:
- ☐ Noticing shapes
- ☐ Calculating/discussing distance
- ☐ Discussing speed limit/miles per hour

Sports:
- ☐ Watching sports (list):
  _____
  _____
- ☐ Keeping track of statistics (list):
  _____
  _____
- ☐ Playing sports (list):
  _____
  _____

Construction activities:
- ☐ Model building
- ☐ Playing with Lego set
- ☐ _____
- ☐ _____

Computer games:
- ☐ _____
- ☐ _____
- ☐ _____
- ☐ _____

Other:
- ☐ _____
- ☐ _____
- ☐ _____
- ☐ _____

Fig. 8.5. Sample questionnaire

Explore the Community

There was a time when all teachers lived within the community in which they taught. This situation is becoming less common as school districts grow in size. For this reason, we sometimes need to make an extra effort to get to know the communities in which our students live. Teachers are encouraged to take mathematical resource walks to examine the types of businesses, activities, and even street signs that are familiar to students within a community (see chapter 10). Record any instances you observe of mathematics in the community, as well as common practices you see.

Using strategies that draw on mathematics embeddedness in activities in the community or in those that have personal relevance for students can be a fruitful way to engage students in realistic and interesting mathematics. Getting to know the lives of your students and their patterns of participation is a great first step in supporting in-school and out-of-school connections and in designing word problems that both connect to individual's lives and support classroom goals such as inclusion, empathy, and social justice. The Math Engagement Framework and Word-problem Expansive Framework can be useful in broadening the types of strategies teachers may already be using.

References

Brenner, Mary E. "Meaning and Money." *Educational Studies in Mathematics* 36, no. 2 (1998): 123–55. doi:10.1023/a:1003176619818

González, Norma, Rosi Andrade, Marta Civil, and Luis Moll. "Bridging Funds of Distributed Knowledge: Creating Zones of Practices in Mathematics." *Journal of Education for Students Placed at Risk (JESPAR)* 6, no. 1–2 (2001): 115–32. doi:10.1207/s15327671espr0601-2_7

Ladson-Billings, Gloria. "Making Mathematics Meaningful in a Multicultural Context." In *New Directions for Equity in Mathematics Education*, edited by Walter. G. Secada, Elizabeth Fennema, and Lisa Byrd Adajian, pp. 126–45. New York: Cambridge University Press, 1995.

Livingston, Gretchen. "Fewer than Half of U.S. Kids Today Live in a 'Traditional' Family." *FactTank: News in the Numbers.* Pew Research Center. December 22, 2014. http://pewrsr.ch/1zW782T

Lobel, Arnold. *Frog and Toad Treasury: Three Books.* New York: HarperCollins, 1970.

LópezLeiva, Carlos A., Zayoni Torres, and Lena L. Khisty. "Acknowledging Spanish and English Resources during Mathematical Reasoning." *Cultural Studies of Science Education* 8, no. 4 (2013): 919–34. doi:10.1007/s11422-013-9518-3

Nasir, Na'ilah Suad. "'Points Ain't Everything': Emergent Goals and Average and Percent Understandings in the Play of Basketball among African American Students." *Anthropology Education Quarterly* 31, no. 3 (2000): 283–305. doi:10.1525/aeq.2000.31.3.283

National Council of Teachers of Mathematics (NCTM). *Principles to Actions: Ensuring Mathematical Success for All.* Reston, Va.: NCTM, 2014.

Renninger, K. Ann, Liza Ewen, and A. K. Lasher. "Individual Interest as Context in Expository Text and Mathematical Word Problems." *Learning and Instruction* 12, no. 4 (2002): 467–90. doi:10.1016/s0959-4752(01)00012-3

Taylor, Edd V. "The Purchasing Practice of Low-Income Students: The Relationship to Mathematical Development." *Journal of the Learning Sciences* 18, no. 3 (2009): 370–415. doi:10.1080/10508400903013462

Turner, Erin, Sylvia Celedón-Pattichis, Mary Marshall, and Alan Tennison. "'Fíjense amorcitos, les voy a contar una historia': The Power of Story to Support Solving and Discussing Mathematical Problems with Latino/a Kindergarten Students." In *Mathematics for Every Student: Responding to Diversity, Grades Pre-K–5*, edited by Dorothy Y. White and Julie S. Spitzer, pp. 23–41. Reston, Va.: National Council of Teachers of Mathematics, 2009.

Wager, Anita A., and David W. Stinson. *Teaching Mathematics for Social Justice: Conversations with Educators*. Reston, Va.: National Council of Teachers of Mathematics, 2012.

CHAPTER 9

Math Thinking Conversations

A Tool for Engaging Teachers and Children in Deep Mathematical Practice

Cassie Freeman, *Teachers College, Columbia University*

Herbert P. Ginsburg, *Teachers College, Columbia University*

Haifa Bautista, *Joan Ganz Cooney Early Learning Program, PrePrep School, New York*

Colleen Uscianowski, *Teachers College, Columbia University*

Haifa Bautista, head of the preschool, is working with five-year-old Rayna (a pseudonym) on an exploration with Unifix cubes. She placed eleven cubes on a plate, and the two discussed how many were present. Then Ms. Bautista asked Rayna to take some away.

Ms. Bautista asked, "So how did you get to only one left?" and Rayna answered, "I took all of them away!" Ms. Bautista followed up: "How many did you take away?" After counting, Rayna concluded, "I took 10 away!" Ms. Bautista continued, "So you took 10 away from 11 and how many's left?" After Rayna answered "one," Ms. Bautista followed up again: "And what happens when you take one away?" Rayna concluded that there would be zero left, even giving a zero sign with her fingers.

This work was supported by a generous grant from the Heising-Simons Foundation.

As their interaction continued, Ms. Bautista explored what Rayna meant when she described taking them all away and getting none left. Using terms such as *a lot* and *some,* Ms. Bautista and Rayna explored what it would mean to take different amounts away. Finally, Rayna demonstrated her understanding of the term zero by referring to it as "nothing."

Ms. Bautista's goal was to find out how five-year-old Rayna was thinking, not to teach her anything specific about subtraction. So she started by asking Rayna to count the objects, then followed up by giving her simple tasks and by probing her thinking.

It is not every day that a school leader sits down to find out what one child knows about mathematics. By taking the time to discover what Rayna knows about subtraction, Ms. Bautista showed her commitment to the teachers and students in her school. The teachers at PrePrep have been developing their expertise in these types of interactions all year, but this was the first time Ms. Bautista video recorded her own Math Thinking Conversation (MTC).

When reflecting on her experience with Rayna, Ms. Bautista had two realizations. One was that

> children can own their own learning and lead the adult into being really the facilitator . . . I had it all planned as to what I was going to work on with her but once we started the conversation I sensed that she has a lot to say about the direction of where she was going . . . she was not hesitant but rather confident. She kind of created the roles for herself and for me. In this clip I felt that my role was to confirm and strengthen while rectifying what she knew so she can move on to the next level.

Her second realization was about teachers:

> I know we need additional PD [professional development] work in letting go of pouring instruction into the children and be confident that children like Rayna can navigate their learning and our role as teachers is to come in at the right time and provide the additional knowledge that will move the children forward in their cognitive and reasoning skills.

Making a Commitment to Access and Equity

Bautista's experience with MTCs is not unique. As they begin these conversations, teachers may come to realize that they need to learn more about children's mathematical thinking and how to assess it so that they can meet the needs of all students through instruction. Having thinking conversations with children also increases teachers' awareness that even young children have ideas worthy of consideration, an important first step to achieving equity in the classroom. Instruction stemming from MTCs can lead to equity in instruction by helping teachers realize the kinds of appropriate accommodations needed for different students and by acknowledging what students already bring to the classroom. The approach to equity of holding students to high standards and providing high support is called for by *Principles and Standards for School Mathematics* (NCTM 2000), a precursor to NCTM's landmark *Principles to Actions: Ensuring Mathematical Success for All* (NCTM 2014). The MTCs do not need to take a great deal of time but do require that teachers pay careful attention to the child's responses and desire to understand what the child knows. Moreover, a school leader communicates the importance of early mathematics education for all students by participating in PD sessions and putting herself in front of the camera with a student.

To place Bautista and Rayna's interaction in context, let us consider the school. PrePrep is a Universal PreKindergarten (UPK) program founded in New York City in 2014 within the Public Prep charter network after a citywide initiative to improve access to pre-K for all children. PrePrep was based on the idea that preschool programs in high-poverty neighborhoods should provide early learning opportunities that can jump-start a child's school career. The school is located in district 7 of the Bronx in New York City, which serves a large, diverse student population. Ninety-three percent of the district's students are from low-income backgrounds; 1 in 10 is homeless; and the average school attendance rate is among the city's lowest. The number of elementary and middle school students demonstrating proficiency is just 10 percent in reading and 13 percent for mathematics—both the lowest of any district in the city (NYC Department of Education 2016). Considering the current situation, all school stakeholders are working diligently to improve the educational opportunities for students in the district.

The mathematics curriculum used in the 2015–2016 school year was based on the Pre-K for All scope and sequence, which aligns with the New York State Prekindergarten Foundation for the Common Core (PKFCC) and articulates clear objectives and high expectations (NYC Department of Education n.d.). The school also adopted the Teaching Strategies Gold Authentic Assessment (Teaching Strategies 2011) so teachers could document observations and use data to guide curriculum planning, differentiate instruction for every student's needs, and reach higher outcomes for each student. Teachers at PrePrep are not very different from teachers in other preschool programs. They have an undergraduate and/or graduate degree in early childhood education but are unlikely to have specialized in mathematics. We have found that most teachers draw on their memory of the mathematics concepts from either high school or a basic college course requirement but could benefit from opportunities to acquire a deeper understanding of the mathematics they need to teach young children.

In order to support the ten staff members at PrePrep, the school began working with the team at Teachers College, Columbia University. The Teachers College (TC) team was interested in supporting early childhood educators develop their understanding of children's mathematical thinking through MTC, which we know to be a powerful tool for entering the child's mind (Ginsburg 1997).

Advancing Access and Equity

Our approach is based on the premise that asking careful questions, considering possible responses and interpretations of them, and recording the interactions can promote deep understanding of children's mathematics. The act of listening to children promotes access and equity by allowing teachers to hear and see what each child brings to the classroom. As diversity should be considered as a resource to improve mathematics learning for all students (Civil 2012), teachers are able, through the act of listening, to understand the diverse experiences that their children bring. Thus, our yearlong PD initiative started with a session on how to have MTCs with young children. These thinking conversations have been described elsewhere as clinical interviews and build on the work of Piaget (Ginsburg 1997). We were concerned that the label "clinical interview" might make teachers uncomfortable because it suggests some kind of pathology or problem, so we decided to change the name to MTC to indicate that these types of interactions can take place anywhere, do not have to last a long time, and represent the kind of high-quality discourse that should be happening across all content areas.

The Math Thinking Conversations

MTCs can take place anywhere, last only as long as the child feels comfortable, and can include a broad set of manipulatives or even none at all. At their heart, these conversations are ways to engage with children to determine what they understand about mathematics as revealed by evidence from their responses to carefully constructed questions and follow-up probes. To have effective conversations, both teacher and child must agree that thinking is important, so that the focus is not on accuracy but on how the child solves problems (Ginsburg 1999).

Following the method described by Piaget, the conversations combine assessment and observation (Ginsburg 1997). The conversation starts with an *initial task*, or question, generally presented the same way for most children. For instance, you may start by asking a child to identify which shapes on a page are triangles. Then, you must *observe* how the child responds to the question. Does she suggest that anything that is "pointy" is a triangle? Does she only identify equilateral triangles (all sides the same length) as triangles? Next, you must quickly *interpret* the child's response. Ask yourself, What did the child's response show me about what she knows, and what should I follow up on? After that brief moment of interpretation, present a new problem that will help you deepen your understanding (theory) of the child's knowledge. If you interpret that the child seems to only identify equilateral triangles, the next step might be to ask why a triangle with exactly two sides the same length is not a triangle. You could follow up with an equilateral triangle that was very small and one that was very big to determine if overall size is part of the child's interpretation. You should repeat the process of question-observe-interpret-question flexibly, introducing new questions as they become relevant.

While this process may seem simple, there are a few important things to keep in mind. First, always start with a task that a child will likely meet with success. This generates a mood of confidence and positions the child as the one in charge of her own thinking. In the vignette, Bautista knew that Rayna was already competent at counting objects in front of her. So when she asked Rayna to take some away, Bautista believed Rayna would be able to use a strategy of counting all that were left to determine the answer. Second, as the tasks and questions get more difficult, make sure the child is attending and trying hard. Bautista frequently asked Rayna to explain her answer further but kept the tone pleasant and fun. Keeping a child motivated when something is difficult requires praising her effort, not her answer, which may well be wrong. Keeping the focus on effort throughout the interview will help the child stay engaged so you can learn more about how she thinks. Third, since the conversation is about thinking, ask the child to describe her thinking. This can be done by asking questions like "How did you do that?" or "How would we prove it to someone?" Sometimes it is difficult for a child to explain her thinking. In order to show the child that you are listening to her and to help her explain her thoughts, use the child's language. For example, a child may not know the word *angle* but can talk about a point or a corner. Respond using the child's language, even if it is not exactly right; this will foster communication. Finally, it is not always the time to teach. These conversations can be used for teaching, but first you must understand how the child thinks before you try to teach her. Try to avoid saying things like "do it this way"; wait for the child to answer. Sometimes children end up spontaneously teaching themselves! Most important to remember, these conversations are never really finished; the child is always learning, and you will always want to know more about what she thinks (Ginsburg 1997).

Thinking Conversations at PrePrep

In order to prepare for the PD that would introduce thinking conversations, the TC team first spent time in classrooms to become familiar with the students and to set them at ease. Then we conducted MTCs with individual students identified as having different levels of number knowledge. The TC team recorded conversations of about ten minutes total with nine different children, using a protocol we developed to determine how high the children were able to count and their ability to count real objects. Unlike a typical assessment, these conversations were designed to get at the "why" of the child's thinking and to see how far a child could go with a little scaffolding. For instance, when asked how high they can count, many children will stop at 10, thinking the task is complete. However, if you ask what comes next and use phrases like "then comes . . . " or "and then . . . " children may be able to show that they have an understanding of the numbers in order beyond 10. Reciting the counting numbers in order is an important first step. Sometimes called rote counting, it lays the foundation for the task—one that many children are often asked to do—of answering the question "How many?" (Early Math Collaborative 2014).

After children count, we dig deeper into their understanding of the number sequence by asking questions such as "What number comes after 7?" or, if we think they can traverse the decade boundary, "What comes after 29?" We then explore the child's ability to enumerate and demonstrate cardinality by giving the child a set of objects and asking "How many?" We follow up by asking how they know, which is frequently the first time children are asked to explain their mathematical thinking. We also look for strategies, such as counting each object only once and moving objects aside as they are counted. Next, we explore if the child can conserve number by having him or her count and then moving the objects around to ask how many again. We also may cover up the objects and ask how many. Here, asking the child how she knows can yield very interesting answers. Some say the strategy they used to determine the original number ("I counted"), while others suggest that we did not add or subtract from the set, so it must be the same. Finally, we ask the children to produce different set sizes such as 2, 3, 5, and 10. In this case, we also ask them to check and change their answers if necessary. Children need to learn that checking is an essential part of doing mathematics.

After making videos of the children talking about counting and cardinality, we made clips showing the variety of student responses to the prompts, as well as how much some students could show they knew with a little prompting. In each PD session, our goal was to use videos showing the students whom the teachers work with every day, both to support teachers in understanding their own children's mathematical thinking and to see what young children are capable of doing.

This first PD session was not just about thinking conversations. We also asked teachers to share mathematical goals for their children and how they would take responsibility for helping their children meet these goals. Finally, we asked them how we could help. Although we had ideas about content and practices teachers might be interested in, we felt that by co-constructing the PD plan with the whole staff of PrePrep, we would have a more effective collaboration (Musanti et al. 2011). In fact, Bautista had very clear goals for supporting teachers in mathematics. Specifically, her objective was "for teachers to deepen their math knowledge, strengthen their skills and confidence in teaching math so they are successful in engaging the children in learning math." In order to meet that objective, the school established a structure that ensures adequate time and consistent opportunities for the children to learn mathematics during twenty-minute instructional centers in addition to the routines at the beginning of the day. Based on our initial conversations, we developed this joint model:

1. Teachers and students talk *together* about mathematics every day.

2. Teachers and students are video recorded doing mathematics twice a month, during whole-class instruction, centers, and free play.

3. TC team records MTCs with children of different needs and abilities twice a month.

4. TC team uses the recordings for PD and provides PrePrep (and potentially parents) with all the videos.

5. After each PD, teachers have "homework," often in the form of specific mathematical conversations to have with students, which TC team then records.

6. PrePrep and TC are partners and can change the PD plans as their needs and interests evolve.

We see this model as a way to promote access by making MTCs central to how mathematics is taught and learned at PrePrep, allowing all staff to participate in the sometimes hard work of thinking mathematically. The frequent use of video ensures that everyone is doing mathematics and allows the PrePrep-TC team to see what works for individual children. The TC team carefully curates the video to highlight interesting student thinking, prompting conversations in PD not just about what children are doing but what evidence we have for how they might be thinking about the mathematics content. In order to truly reach all the children, it is important to engage not only the teachers but also the other school staff. To that end, the teachers, assistant teachers, the parent coordinator, and the school office manager attend these sessions.

Professional Development at PrePrep

Two Fridays a month, the TC team leads a one and a half hour PD at PrePrep. Each session addresses a content area (e.g., counting, shapes, patterns) that was determined by PrePrep. The sessions start with an introduction to the mathematics and the Big Ideas, as described by the Early Math Collaborative (Early Math Collaborative 2014). We show video clips of a variety of children, at different places in the learning trajectory, demonstrating their thinking for each of the Big Ideas. As teachers watch the clips, they write down evidence of the child's thinking and then we discuss what the evidence suggests about the child's understanding. Next, we talk about how to use this knowledge to shape instruction. During these conversations, TC facilitators rephrase teachers' comments with specific terminology to help teachers develop a shared mathematical lexicon.

While mathematics terminology and concepts are an essential part of every session, we also discuss other aspects of the teacher-child interaction that could be used to shape instruction. For instance, some children in the school felt more comfortable speaking Spanish than English. Since many of the teachers were also Spanish speakers, we discussed shifting the language of the conversation when appropriate (see chapters 2, 3, and 4). This flexibility in language use gives teachers the chance to really understand what the child knows and communicates to the child that she brings valuable ideas to a conversation, regardless of the language she uses. Additionally, this flexibility indicates our shared commitment to the productive belief that "students who are not fluent in English can learn the language of mathematics at grade level or beyond at the same time that they are learning English when appropriate instructional strategies are used" (Ramirez and Celedón-Pattichis 2012; NCTM 2014, p. 63). Further, some children in the school were hesitant to speak at all or used very few words to explain their thinking. Therefore, teachers and TC facilitators talked about the importance of observing the child's gestures in all MTCs. Gestures not only indicate what a child understands but also indicate a readiness to learn concepts (Domínguez 2010; Fernandes and McLeman 2012; Goldin-Meadow 2015). By not limiting MTC interactions to spoken English, teachers empower students to "participate meaningfully" in the mathematical conversations and later on in classroom discourse (NCTM 2014).

Because our PD is meant to affect teaching starting the following Monday, teachers practice with one another the conversational prompts and strategies we have used with their children. Teachers take turns being the teacher and the child. When taking on the role of the child and to make using the protocol more authentic, the teacher considers either a particular child in his or her class or a type of child that he or she might encounter. Sometimes it is still difficult to know what kinds of questions will help a child explain her thinking. To that end, we recommend a few types of questions for teachers to use:

- Predicting: What would happen if we . . .

- Explanation: Why did that happen?

- Explanation to a "little kid": How would you help a little kid understand how this works? What would you tell her?

- Counterfactual (reasoning about alternatives): What if you did not remember the sum of 2 + 3? How would you figure it out?

After teachers complete the role play, we come together to discuss the experience paying particular attention to answering questions about how we know what the child knows. It is our goal that teachers become seekers of evidence to support their judgments about children's knowledge.

Finally, we close the PD with a reflection and a homework assignment. The homework usually involves asking teachers to try out some of the strategies and prompts suggested in PD. Then, when the TC team returns, they can answer teachers' questions, give feedback, and assist with implementation. The next week, the cycle begins again with the TC team coming in to record teachers and children and have thinking conversations to inform the next PD.

In addition to the observation, recording, and PD, the TC team regularly meets with Bautista to talk about particular needs for particular students and teachers. These conversations allow us to problem solve together, both for the TC team to become better at providing the assistance the PrePrep team needs and for the PrePrep team to constantly consider how they can bring a higher level of mathematics to all children. Finally, since all the PD sessions are recorded, the TC team revisits particular parts of the session to gather clips for our own learning. For instance, when we try out a new activity with teachers, sometimes it is difficult to know how well it is working in the moment. We review our PD sessions and discussions with the PrePrep team, and we refine our methods for the next sessions and for PD sessions with other schools.

Meeting Challenges

Camera shyness and critique. Even as teacher certification programs increasingly turn to the use of videos of teaching, teachers still feel nervous when someone comes in the room with the camera. The TC team members knew that we had to build trust before we could capture authentic interactions between children and teachers. As described above, we spent a few weeks just "hanging out" in the classroom, talking to children during free play and centers and casually talking with the teachers. Then we started by recording our own conversations with children. After the teachers saw that we were willing to share videos of our conversations, even highlighting where we would like to do things differently, we approached them about casually recording what the children were doing. Of course, when children are working with a teacher, you cannot help but record the teacher as well (or at least her voice). When teachers saw the clips in the PDs, we made sure to have every classroom represented and to talk about the productive interactions that were happening along with where we saw opportunities to follow up more with children.

Many teachers find it difficult to talk frankly about what they see in the video clips of other teachers. This was complicated by the fact that the school was only in its second year and the teachers had not been together for long. In order to help teachers, we tried to refocus on what different lessons and questioning strategies demonstrated about students' knowledge. In this way, using the question prompts we use with children during MTC can be helpful. Asking a predicting question such as "What would happen if you asked the child . . ." can allow teachers to think critically about their questioning without invoking blame. For example, when a teacher asked a child the follow-up question "How do you know?" and the child answered, "I just know," the teacher stopped probing, unsure of how to follow up. When we asked the group a counterfactual question, namely, what the child might have done in response to a different probe, teachers volunteered that the focus teacher could have asked, "How would you explain this to a little kid?" We then talked about possible answers to that question and how they might have helped the teacher understand more of the child's thinking. Developing teacher comfort with video and analyzing that video with others takes time and constant reminders that we use this tool in order to increase student learning. If we do not document our practice, we can never see our change.

Planning for engaging all children. Part of equity is giving every child what he or she needs to participate meaningfully in learning mathematics (NCTM 2014). However, in order to know what a child needs, teachers must know where the child is. Teachers used the MTC to determine children's initial knowledge and then proceeded to work with individual children during center time. While one of four students was engaged with the teacher, the others were left to their own devices, which was not an effective learning environment. The teachers recognized that they were not engaging all children but did not know how to pull the children together when they were at different levels of understanding. In fact, some tacitly held the unproductive belief that equity was the same as equality and wanted to give the children the same opportunities for fairness (NCTM 2014). However, we worked together to move toward the more productive belief that students should receive differentiated supports, even receiving different scaffolds for activities while in a group with other children (NCTM 2014). Together with Bautista, the

TC team developed a strategy of clarifying learning outcomes before starting a mathematics center. The strategy focused on four questions:

1. Who is in the group? PrePrep is dedicated to having small groups of diverse learners. The first task was for teachers to plan who would be in a group, not just based on which children liked to be together but how they could best learn from each other.

2. What do they know? As MTCs were becoming a ubiquitous feature of the classroom, teachers were more confident about their children's knowledge. Using this question, teachers planned prompts focused on what they thought the group members knew, with flexibility to change the prompts as they discovered more about the children's thinking.

3. What will they learn? This is the instructional goal of the center. Rather than thinking about centers in terms of an activity to be completed, teachers were pushed to find evidence that their activities were aligned with the New York pre-K standards.

4. How will we know? Since having MTCs is all about gathering evidence to interpret what a child knows, teachers considered what exactly a child might do that would help them understand if the child was meeting the instructional goal of the center.

This level of planning was new for the teachers at PrePrep and took some time to implement. We expected that this would be difficult, so we created the questions using simple, easy-to-remember language. When the TC team visited, they would ask the teachers these questions in order to stress the importance of the approach but also to consider how well this was working for the teachers. The TC team would then compare notes with Bautista, who was asking the same questions as she observed classrooms throughout the week.

Increasing rigor. When we first started working together, many children at PrePrep were able to do much more than was asked of them in mathematics. You will find this to be true in the great majority of schools. Some teachers recognized that a few children were bored with the content but felt ill-equipped to do more with their children. Moreover, sometimes rigor is described in opposition to what is "developmentally appropriate." Some teachers were concerned that increasing rigor would mean that children would no longer get to explore and play. The TC team does not see rigor and developmentally appropriate practice in opposition. In fact, we subscribe to what Brown and Mowry (2015) describe as "rigorous developmentally appropriate practice." This approach to instruction asks early childhood educators to use practices that reflect their understanding of child development and individual children's unique and sociocultural needs to teach knowledge and skills that they expect all children to attain and demonstrate (Brown and Mowry 2015). We focused on the idea of understanding each learner (through the information gathered in the MTCs) to offer challenges to each child. Since the teachers used centers to do most of their mathematics instruction, we worked together to develop prompts and questions that would meet children where they were and push them further, with support. Subscribing to the premise of high expectations for all students, coupled with individualized supports, we hoped to eliminate gaps in access to rigorous mathematics education that exist in so many high-poverty schools (NCTM 2014). For instance, many children were only doing AB patterns in class. However, after having MTCs with individual children, the TC team determined that many children were ready to try more complex patterns. PrePrep teachers then used a TC-developed protocol (see Appendix) to have MTCs that stressed identifying, copying, completing, extending, describing, and translating patterns with increasingly complex repeating patterns and growing patterns (e.g., using a rule of +1).

Our model, based on MTC, encourages teachers to have meaningful interactions with children around mathematics, use what they learn about the child's understanding, and build on the understanding to promote access and equity in mathematics for all children.

Reflecting and Taking Action

As you have read through our experiences, we hope you consider the same questions we asked the PrePrep teachers to consider:

- What do you expect your students to be able to do mathematically?
- What evidence will you seek to understand what your students are thinking?
- How will this evidence change how you promote your children's learning?

In addition to answering the questions, consider taking the following actions:

- Set up a time and space to have conversations with individual children or small groups, starting at the beginning of the year. This can be done during centers, free-choice time, snack time, or almost any other occasion (except nap time!).

- Record your MTCs and discuss them regularly with other teachers. While it is not always feasible to video record your children, you can certainly take notes and gather artifacts as evidence, in order to understand their mathematical thinking.

- Revisit the conversations regularly. Very young children can learn a lot over relatively brief periods of time. If you are frequently revisiting the MTC, you will see changes as your children develop their abilities to explain their thoughts, even as they become more complex.

- Make sure you are including every child in a conversation. Access to deep mathematical thinking is for everyone. Different approaches to engagement may be needed for different children. For instance, not every child will find it easy to answer a question like "How do you know?" Try different questioning strategies and approaches so that each child can show how he or she thinks.

- Give parents videos that demonstrate their children's mathematics competence. Sharing videos of children showing what they know can help parents appreciate the hard work their children are doing and have their own thinking conversations with their children.

MTC can be a powerful tool for promoting access to rigorous mathematics learning for all children. When schools and teachers take time to ask thoughtful questions to understand children's thinking, they can create instructional plans to help all children move forward, increasing equity.

References

Brown, Christopher P., and Brian Mowry. "Close Early Learning Gaps with Rigorous DAP." *Phi Delta Kappan* 96, no. 7 (2015): 53.

Civil, Marta. "Mathematics Teaching and Learning of Immigrant Students: An Overview of the Research Field Across Multiple Settings." In *Opening the Cage: Critique and Politics of Mathematics Education,* edited by Ole Skovsmose and Brian Greer, pp. 127–42. Rotterdam, The Netherlands: Sense Publishers, 2012.

Domínguez, Higinio. "Bilingual Students' Articulation and Gesticulation of Mathematical Knowledge during Problem Solving." *Bilingual Research Journal* 29, no. 2 (2010): 269–93.

Early Math Collaborative. *Big Ideas of Early Mathematics: What Teachers of Young Children Need to Know.* New York: Pearson, 2014.

Fernandes, Anthony, and Laura McLeman. "Interpreting and Using Gestures of English Language Learners in Mathematics Teaching." *Teaching for Excellence and Equity in Mathematics* 4, no. 1 (2012): 15–23.

Ginsburg, Herbert P. *Entering the Child's Mind: The Clinical Interview in Psychological Research and Practice.* Cambridge, United Kingdom: Cambridge University Press, 1997.

———. "The Do's and Don'ts of Clinical Interviewing." Course document from "HUDK 4027: Development of Mathematical Thinking." Teachers College, Columbia University. 1999.

Goldin-Meadow, Susan. "From Action to Abstraction: Gesture as a Mechanism of Change." *Developmental Review* 38, (2015): 167–84. doi: 10.1016/j.dr.2015.07.007

Musanti, Sandra, Mary Marshall, Karla Ceballos, and Sylvia Celedón-Pattichis. "Situating Mathematics Professional Development: A Bilingual Teacher and Researchers' Collaboration." In *Latinos and Mathematics Education: Research on Learning and Teaching in Classrooms and Communities*, edited by Kip Téllez, Judit Moschkovich, and Marta Civil, pp. 215–32. Charlotte, N.C.: Information Age, 2011.

National Council of Teachers of Mathematics (NCTM). *Principles and Standards for School Mathematics*. Reston, Va.: NCTM, 2000.

———.*Principles to Actions: Ensuring Mathematical Success for All*. Reston, Va.: NCTM, 2014.

NYC Department of Education. "Data about Schools." Last modified December 31, 2016. http://schools.nyc.gov/AboutUs/schools/data/default.htm

NYC Department of Education. "Pre-K for All Program Quality Standards." N.d. http://schools.nyc.gov/NR/rdonlyres/175F24FE-E23E-4B93-BF6C-0C4EF35663D2/0/NYC_PreK_for_All_Quality_Standards.pdf

Ramirez, Nora, and Sylvia Celedón-Pattichis. "Second Language Development and Implications for the Mathematics Classroom." In *Beyond Good Teaching: Advancing Mathematics Education for ELLs*, edited by Nora Ramirez and Sylvia Celedón-Pattichis, pp. 19–37. Reston, Va.: National Council of Teachers of Mathematics, 2012.

Teaching Strategies. *Teaching Strategies GOLD: Fast Facts for Decision Makers.* Bethesda, Md.: Teaching Strategies, 2011. http://shop.teachingstrategies.com/content/pageDocs/teaching-strategies-gold-assessment-FAQs.pdf

Appendix: Patterns Protocol

Recommended age range: 3–8 years

Note: For older children, repeating patterns may be too easy. Make it more appropriate for their age by using more complicated patterns such as growing patterns.

- Show the child a pattern, such as 3 repeating units of a frog and a hat. Scatter picture cards of frogs and hats on the table and ask the child to continue the pattern. Possible questions: How did you decide to put the cards the way you did? What would go next? How do you know? Can you tell me about this pattern? What does it always do?

- Make a mistake in a pattern and see if the child can recognize the mistake. (You may need to tell him/her that you have made a mistake and you want him/her to check.) What was not right about what you did?

- Scatter another set of cards or manipulatives on the table that allow the child to make a pattern and ask the child to make his or her own pattern. Can you tell me about your pattern?

- What is a pattern? What if you wanted to teach someone else how to make a pattern, what would you say to him or her?

Create another type of pattern, such as a growing pattern. What comes next? How do you know? For older children, supply cards that tell the position number, and ask what design belongs in different positions farther down the line. Would you know how to make the design for *any* position number? How?

CHAPTER 10

Connecting Children's Mathematical Thinking with Children's Backgrounds, Knowledge, and Experiences in Mathematics Instruction

Tonya Gau Bartell, *Michigan State University*

Mary Q. Foote, *Queens College of the City University of New York*

Amy Roth McDuffie, *Washington State University*

Erin E. Turner, *The University of Arizona*

Julia M. Aguirre, *University of Washington–Tacoma*

Corey Drake, *Michigan State University*

While exploring the neighborhood around their school in a community walk (one of the three activities to be described in this chapter), teachers saw flyers for a carnival and realized it would be taking place in the coming weeks only a few miles from the school (Aguirre et al. 2013; Turner et al. 2015). Thinking that they might be able to make connections between this community event and meaningful mathematics for their second-grade students, the teachers worked to get to know their

This work is based on research supported by the National Science Foundation under grant #1228034. Any opinions, findings, conclusions, or recommendations expressed in this material are those of the authors and do not necessarily reflect the views of the National Science Foundation.

students by eliciting prior experiences with this and other carnivals. They discovered that their students had attended this church carnival or other carnivals in the past and that many planned to attend the upcoming local carnival. They also discovered that their students preferred certain rides, such as the "dragon coaster," and that students were often unable to go on all of the rides because they spent all their tickets.

Drawing on what they learned, the teachers planned a series of high cognitive demand mathematical tasks (i.e., tasks that require students to engage in thinking and reasoning; Smith and Stein 1998) about different ways to spend a given number of tickets at the carnival (see fig. 10.1). How to spend a given number of tickets would matter to the children because they had experienced running out of tickets before they were able to go on all the rides they wanted.

Buy in or hook → It matters to the kids

 # Task

Today you are going to the Maple Lane Carnival. Your parents have given you 25 tickets to spend on rides and food. There are four rides and two food stands in which you can spend your tickets. The prices are:
- Popcorn stand- 1 ticket
- Cotton candy stand- 2 tickets
- Big slide- 2 tickets
- Ferris wheel- 3 tickets
- Motorcycle carousel ride- 4 tickets
- Dragon roller coaster- 5 tickets

You must figure out two different ways you would want to spend all 25 of your tickets.

Extension Task:

Suppose you are going to the carnival again. This time you have 30 tickets and there are four rides. The roller coaster costs 9 tickets, the carousel costs 8 tickets, the Ferris wheel costs 7 tickets, and the Funnel cake stand costs 1 ticket. What are two different ways you can spend all of your 30 tickets?

Fig. 10.1. Carnival task

Specifically, one of the lesson's mathematical learning goals was that students would understand that a number (in this case, 25) can be decomposed in a variety of ways. Attending to children's mathematical thinking in their lesson plan, the teachers documented strategies they anticipated their students might use to solve these tasks, such as guess-and-check, repeated addition (to go on the same ride multiple times), incremental subtraction, and partitioning (dividing the set of 25 tickets into small sets and then deciding how to spend each group of tickets, such as some on food and some on rides). These mathematical ideas reflect the Common Core State Standards for Mathematics (CCSSM) for second-grade students (i.e., 2.OA.A.1, 2.OA.C.3; NGA Center and CCSSO, 2010). In consideration of whether the task would be accessible to all students, the teachers identified in advance some of the struggles students might have. Recognizing that some students might not find a combination that uses the entire set of 25 tickets or that some students might need to directly model possible combinations, the teachers provided concrete materials for them.

Thinking ahead + Scaffolding

The teachers also planned to elicit and build on children's community experiences with the carnival throughout the lesson. For example, they planned to launch the lesson by inviting students to share carnival experiences, including how they made decisions about rides and food and whether they ever ran out of tickets. Furthermore, to make the task accessible, the first time the "figure out two ways to spend 25 tickets" task was posed, they planned for students to role-play spending tickets by visiting carnival ride stands placed throughout the classroom (see fig. 10.2) and leaving the required number of tickets at each stand.

Fig. 10.2. Carnival ride and food stands

Students would then be given an opportunity to plan two different ways to spend exactly 25 tickets. Finally, the teachers planned to orchestrate a whole-class discussion where multiple students would share their strategies and solutions, specifically facilitating discussion around different ways to get to 25, or "different combinations of rides and food."

In getting to know their kindergarteners, teachers learned that many of the students spent time at the local YMCA. When visiting the local YMCA on a community walk in an effort to learn about mathematical practices in the neighborhood (Aguirre et al. 2013; Turner et al. 2015), the teachers noticed that many children loved to play Musical Hula Hoops. In this game, the music starts and a locomotor movement is called (e.g., skipping, galloping, sliding); children move randomly throughout the activity area that is laden with Hula Hoops. They may not enter a hoop while the music is playing. When the music stops, children immediately move inside a hoop. More than one child can be in a hoop at the same time. To start the next round, children step outside the hoops; three or four hoops are removed, and the process starts again. The game ends when all the players have squeezed into two or three hoops. The teachers decided to design a mathematics lesson that would engage students in meaningful mathematics and that would connect to their experiences playing Musical Hula Hoops.

The teachers designed a series of mathematical tasks to be used with their kindergarteners, the first of which would guide their class discussion around the different ways one could decompose the number 10 (see problem 1 in fig. 10.3). Attending to mathematical thinking in their plan, the teachers designed a high cognitive demand task (Smith and Stein 1998) with numbers (e.g., 10, 8) that was appropriate for students at this grade level and that connected to the CCSSM (i.e., K.OA.A.3). One possible challenge teachers anticipated was that some students might struggle in their understanding of the phrase "in each." To address this challenge, teachers thought some students could act out the game as a way to directly model the mathematics.

[handwritten margin note: Noted possible struggles]

The teachers also planned to elicit and build on children's lived experiences throughout the lesson. For example, they planned to launch the lesson by sharing with the students that they had visited the YMCA and by asking who in the room had played Musical Hula Hoops. To support students who had not played this game at the YMCA and to aid all students who might want to directly model the mathematics, the teachers planned to begin the lesson by playing Musical Hula Hoops. A number of hoops were available in the classroom, as well as sheets of paper with images of Hula Hoops. Finally, they planned to facilitate a whole-class discussion where students shared their responses and strategies to problem 1 (see fig. 10.3) and together discussed, "How many different ways have we seen our classmates arrange the number 10?"

Problem 1

There is a group of 10 students and there are 3 Hula Hoops. Show us a way to make sure that there is a student in every Hula Hoop. You can use blocks, circles, pictures, and anything you need to show your brilliance.

Problem 2

There are 4 Hula Hoops and 2 students standing in each Hula Hoop. How many students are standing in the Hula Hoops?

Problem 3

There are 8 students and 2 Hula Hoops with 3 students standing each. How many students are not standing in a Hula Hoop?

Fig. 10.3. Hula Hoop task

Advancing Access and Equity

Effective mathematics instruction for all students must be both "responsive to students' backgrounds, experiences and knowledge" (NCTM 2014, p. 60) and focused on "meaningful mathematics learning" (p. 61) as opposed to rote skills and procedures. As teachers acquire knowledge of children's mathematical thinking (e.g., strategies for solving story problems, common confusions), they can make productive changes in classroom practices, which then support children's learning of mathematics (Carpenter et al. 1989; Jacobs and Ambrose 2008). Additionally, children benefit from mathematics instruction that is responsive to and builds upon their cultural and community-based knowledge in mathematically meaningful ways.

Research, professional development, and teacher preparation programs, however, tend to isolate these two topics, sometimes focusing on children's mathematical thinking and other times on their home- and community-based knowledge. Working along these two dimensions simultaneously may reveal opportunities for promoting equity that are unrealized when knowledge of children's mathematical thinking and their home- and community-based knowledge are considered separately (Turner et al. 2012). That is, teachers can learn to draw upon these multiple knowledge bases as a resource for learning during mathematics instruction.

The two vignettes above provide examples of mathematics instruction that integrates a focus on both meaningful mathematics and students' experiences and knowledge. The vignettes illustrate meaningful mathematics through the use of appropriate tasks requiring high levels of cognitive demand (Smith and Stein 1998) and lessons allowing for multiple student solution strategies and the discussion of those strategies and students' mathematical thinking. The vignettes also illustrate being "responsive to students' backgrounds, experiences, and knowledge" (NCTM 2014, p. 60) by connecting to activities familiar to children (spending tickets at the carnival, playing Musical Hula Hoops) and having space in each lesson to directly elicit children's knowledge of such contexts (e.g., asking students to share carnival experiences or share if they have played Musical Hula Hoops; see chapter 3 for more connections to this work).

In this chapter, we suggest three activities—getting to know your students, engaging with the community, and creating mathematics lessons—that can help teachers build connections between children's backgrounds, experiences, and knowledge and children's mathematical thinking in their instructional planning (see chapters 2, 7, and 8). The vignettes reflect the work of teachers when they engaged in these three activities and worked toward equitable mathematics instruction.

This work can be challenging for teachers, particularly when the lived experiences of teachers and their students are dissimilar (Ladson-Billings 1995). Because of this, teachers may not be engaging in an important component of effective teaching for diverse learners: recognizing, eliciting, and building on children's strengths and knowledge, such as children's mathematical thinking and their cultural and community-based knowledge. We thus suggest these three activities, based on research done by the TEACH Math Project with prospective and practicing teachers (Turner et al. 2012). These activities can help teachers build connections between schools and communities in ways that honor children's multiple knowledge bases in their instructional planning. Working to build such connections can support a strength-based perspective of students, families, and communities that supports children's learning of mathematics.

Getting to Know Your Students

Elementary teachers usually make efforts to know the children they teach, and this information can support mathematics teaching and learning. We found getting to know one's students, either through an interview or informal conversations, to be an important first step in supporting teachers to learn about children's communities. Table 10.1 includes sets of questions that our participants used when getting to know students in the classroom. These questions helped teachers in the above vignettes learn about their students' experiences with carnivals and about what many of them did at the YMCA. The first set of questions focuses on identifying places, locations, and activities in the community familiar to the child. When asked these questions, children tended to share information about their family and friends, such as the names and numbers of family members and playmates; about community settings, such as local businesses they pass on the way to and from school (gas station, corner bakery, the "candy man"); about where and how they spend time after school (grandma's house, playing video games); or about community locations they might go to with their families (parks, grocery stores, museums, library, YMCA). Children also identified things they do at home, though generally not with much detail (cooking, laundry, dancing, playing, gaming). Children rarely described their activities in ways that made mathematical ideas and processes explicit; rather, teachers used the community walk activity described later to look for such mathematical ideas and processes.

The second set of questions focuses on children's ideas, attitudes, and dispositions toward mathematics. Children generally described what they are good at or what they like or dislike about mathematics, such as "I am good at addition." Almost all students talked about mathematics as being important, and they often connected this to "future careers" (generally not naming a specific job) or to everyday experiences, such as counting and making purchases (e.g., "to learn to count up to 1,000" or "to give the right amount of money"). When considering people they know who are good at mathematics, children generally identified other students in their classes and noted that these students were "fast" or "good at explaining." When describing why it is hard for some people to learn mathematics, however, they did not tend to focus on individuals but instead noted that mathematics is "tricky," "confusing," and that it "requires you to think." A difficult question for children to answer was how they use mathematics outside of school. They talked about getting homework help from teachers, parents, grandparents, and siblings and saw mathematics homework as the primary way they "did" mathematics outside of school. Some students also mentioned using mathematics to calculate time or to make purchases.

Table 10.1. Questions to support knowing your students

Questions about children's home and community knowledge bases and resources

- If I were going to walk from school to your house, what are some things or places that I would see?
- Where do you like to go with family or friends? What do you do there? Where do you like to go on the weekends with your family?
- What kinds of things do you do with family/friends at home—both regular routines (cooking) and things you enjoy (games)?
- What are some places close to school that you have been to? What do you do at those places?
- Can you think of any places in the community where people do math or use math? What about your family members, where do they use math? Where do they do math?

Questions about children's ideas and dispositions related to mathematics

- What are some things in math that you are really good at? What is something in math that you are not as good at? How do you know?
- What are some things in math that you really like? What about math do you not like?
- Do you think it is important to learn math? Why do you think so?
- How would you describe what math is? (e.g., describe to a younger sibling)
- Who do you know that is good in math? How do you know? What makes that person good in math?
- Why do you think it is hard for some people to learn math?
- Do you use math outside of school? How?
- Who helps you with math if you get stuck in class? At home? How do they help you?

We have found that asking these questions in informal conversations helps children feel at ease and share about themselves and that these conversations can happen all in one sitting or in smaller interactions over time. These findings have led to some suggestions for teachers who want to engage in this work, which we articulate now. Begin by interviewing one or two students in your classroom. Since teachers have an easier time developing relationships with children who are like them (Spindler and Spindler 1982), we found that teachers learned the most when they chose a child who was different from them in one or more sociocultural ways (gender, race, socioeconomic status, home language). You might also select as your first child one who does not live in your own community or who is struggling in your mathematics class and whom you wish to support by making efforts to connect in new ways to his or her mathematical thinking and community-based knowledge.

Engaging with the Community

After learning more about the children in your mathematics classroom, including identifying community locations that are familiar to them, a next step is to go on a community walk and to visit some locations identified by students. As illustrated in the vignettes, this engagement with the community supports teachers to become "aware of the presence and uses of mathematics in the students' communities" (Leonard and Guha 2002, p. 115). It is also an opportunity to look for mathematical practices and mathematical funds of knowledge, such as deciding how to spend 25 tickets or strategizing in a Hula Hoop game, which can be used to design a problem solving–based mathematics lesson. Conversations with children based on the aforementioned questions, as well as other discussions in the school setting with students, parents, or family members, provide critical information about locations to visit for the community walk. Table 10.2 includes an excerpt of the guidelines for the community walk (Turner et al. 2015).

Table 10.2. Community walk guidelines

Visit at least two different sites in the community.
Examples include parks, stores, community health centers, cultural centers, churches, banks, military base, factories or processing plants, bakeries, construction sites, restaurants, corner stores, and so forth.
Look for and document evidence of mathematics.
Evidence could include people using mathematics, mathematical concepts or principles "in action," mathematical practices, and so on. Talk to individuals who work, play, or shop in the setting about how they use mathematics. Take or draw pictures and take field notes. Identify how each picture or experience you document provides evidence of mathematics.
Formulate a series of questions about the contexts you visited that could be investigated mathematically.
Start by reviewing the pictures, artifacts, and notes that you took. Then brainstorm a list of possible questions and data sources that could be used to answer those questions. Try to generate questions that "matter" (Turner and Strawhun 2007) or are authentic. These should be questions that you, students, or someone else who works, visits, or plays in the setting actually encounters and would want answered.

As noted, children often do not describe their activities in ways that make explicit their mathematical ideas and processes. Rather, as in the above vignettes, to make community connections, teachers might have to analyze children's and families' (and others') practices in the setting (e.g., deciding how to spend exactly 25 tickets) to identify possible mathematical connections. In another example, a prospective teacher pair who went on a community walk with their cooperating teacher and her first-grade son learned that many students walk to school and prefer particular routes because they include shortcuts. While the child did not describe in detail how he figured which routes were the "fastest," the teacher recognized that comparing different routes to school was an authentic activity for children that involved mathematical ideas, such as measuring and comparing distances (connecting to the CCSSM 1.MD.A.1 and 1.MD.A.2).

You can also draw on your experiences in a community setting and imagine ways children and families might use mathematics. For example, other teachers visited a local Mexican bakery that their students had told them about in previous conversations. The teachers explained, "We noticed that the store had almost everything necessary for a birthday party. The store had piñatas, candy for the piñata, as well as their well-known (within the community) *pasteles de tres leches*, three-milk cakes" (Turner et al. 2014, p. 38). The teachers reflected on how they might use mathematics when planning a birthday party and designed a lesson revolving around planning a birthday party with supplies from the Mexican bakery as a context to connect to cultural practices surrounding birthday celebrations.

We have found that teachers need to be careful not to assume that they know where children go and what locations are important to children and families in their communities; teachers need to ask and listen for this information. Visits might include observing people using mathematics or talking with people who work, play, or shop in the community about how they use mathematics in that setting. We have also found it helpful for teachers to take pictures as they engage with the community as a way both to document evidence of mathematics and to elicit more details about children's experiences. Teachers can take the photos and document how each picture demonstrates evidence of mathematics, or they might bring the photos to the classroom and let students share their own knowledge about and experiences from those settings, potentially furthering teachers' knowledge of the mathematical practices of children in a particular context.

Creating Mathematics Lessons

After taking community walks, a next step is to design a problem solving–based mathematics lesson or task(s) to deepen children's mathematical understanding of a particular concept connected to the community context. Teachers might think about the mathematical practices used in the setting and the appropriate grade-level mathematical learning goals related to such practices. You may choose to first find a mathematics task in your textbook and adapt it to the context (see Drake et al. 2015), or you might design a new task that meets particular mathematical objectives for your grade level. The two vignettes at the start of the chapter provide examples of lesson plans that connect school mathematics (i.e., aligned to curriculum standards, such as the CCSSM) and knowledge of children's communities (e.g., the church carnival, the Hula Hoop game) in mathematics instructional planning.

Agree

We have found that starting small can be beneficial for teachers in creating mathematical tasks or lessons based on their engagement with the community and their knowledge of students. For example, teachers may begin by looking for existing resources in the curriculum materials that are not part of the main lesson, such as problem extensions or connections for English language learners, that might provide additional insights about connections to children's community and cultural funds of knowledge or mathematical thinking (see Drake et al. 2015).

Reflecting and Taking Action

In this chapter, we examined ideas for promoting mathematics learning for students by the integration of children's mathematical thinking and their community-based knowledge. When reflecting on your instructional practice, consider the following questions:

- In what ways do my instructional practices recognize and build on the knowledge and strengths students bring to the classroom? How did the use of those resources influence students' learning?

- What resources and knowledge (e.g., mathematical, cultural, community, family, linguistic) did students draw upon to understand and solve the mathematics task?

- Where are opportunities for students to make sense of the mathematics and develop or use their own solution strategies and approaches?

- What kinds of spaces exist for students with varied mathematical and linguistic backgrounds and confidences to share and discuss their mathematical thinking with the teacher and the class?

- What are the opportunities for activating or connecting to family/cultural/community knowledge in each phase of the lesson (i.e., launch, explore, summarize)?

We suggest three activities or actions that teachers can take to begin to support such work beyond the aforementioned reflection on practice: getting to know students; engaging in community walks; and creating mathematics lessons that integrate these foci. Consider getting to know one or two students in your classroom with whom you have not yet fully connected. Perhaps you can talk with them for a few minutes before or after school or engage in a conversation with them and a parent or guardian during student pickup time. Visit one community location multiple times, perhaps with a colleague, taking photos if appropriate.

Discuss the photos with your students and colleagues and begin brainstorming mathematical connections. Although making meaningful connections based on these experiences may be difficult in your initial lesson planning, these actions can help you reorient your thinking toward students and communities. These kinds of changes in thinking can be important first steps in drawing on knowledge that students bring to the classroom to construct meaningful problem-based mathematics lessons.

References

Aguirre, Julia M., Erin E. Turner, Tonya G. Bartell, Crystal K. Craig, Mary Q. Foote, Amy Roth McDuffie, and Corey Drake. "Making Connections in Practice: How Prospective Elementary Teachers Connect to Children's Mathematical Thinking and Community Funds of Knowledge in Mathematics Instruction." *Journal of Teacher Education* 64, no. 2 (2013): 178–92.

Carpenter, Thomas P., Elizabeth Fennema, Penelope L. Peterson, Chi-Pang Chiang, and Megan Loef. "Using Knowledge of Children's Mathematics Thinking in Classroom Teaching: An Experimental Study." *American Educational Research Journal* 26, no. 4 (1989): 499–531.

Drake, Corey, Tonia Land, Tonya G. Bartell, Julia M. Aguirre, Mary Q. Foote, Amy Roth McDuffie, and Erin Turner. "Three Strategies for Opening Curriculum Spaces." *Teaching Children Mathematics* 21, no. 6 (2015): 346–53.

Jacobs, Victoria, and Rebecca Ambrose. "Making the Most of Story Problems." *Teaching Children Mathematics* 15, no. 5 (2008): 260–66.

Ladson-Billings, Gloria. "Toward a Theory of Culturally Relevant Pedagogy." *American Educational Research Journal* 32, no. 3 (1995): 465–91.

Leonard, Jacqueline, and Smita Guha. "Creating Cultural Relevance in Teaching and Learning Mathematics." *Teaching Children Mathematics* 9, no. 2 (2002): 114–18.

National Council of Teachers of Mathematics (NCTM). *Principles to Actions: Ensuring Mathematical Success for All.* Reston, Va.: NCTM, 2014.

National Governors Association Center for Best Practices and Council of Chief State School Officers (NGA Center and CCSSO). *Common Core State Standards for Mathematics.* Washington, D.C.: NGA Center and CCSSO, 2010. http://www.corestandards.org

Smith, Margaret Schwan, and Mary Kay Stein. "Selecting and Creating Mathematical Tasks: From Research to Practice." *Mathematics Teaching in the Middle School* 3, no. 5 (1998): 344–50.

Spindler, George, and Louise Spindler. "Roger Harker and Schonhausen: From the Familiar to the Strange and Back Again." In *Doing the Ethnography of Schooling*, edited by George Spindler, pp. 20–46. Prospect Heights, Ill.: Waveland, 1982.

Turner, Erin, and Beatriz T. Font Strawhun. "Posing Problems That Matter: Investigating School Overcrowding." *Teaching Children Mathematics* 13, no. 9 (2007): 457–62.

Turner, Erin E., Julia M. Aguirre, Tonya G. Bartell, Corey Drake, Mary Q. Foote, and Amy Roth McDuffie. "Making Meaningful Connections with Mathematics and the Community: Lessons from Pre-service Teachers." In *TODOS Research Monograph 3: Embracing*

Resources of Children, Families, Communities and Cultures in Mathematics Learning, edited by Tonya Gau Bartell and Alfinio Flores, pp. 30–49. Tempe, Ariz.: TODOS: Mathematics for All, 2014.

Turner, Erin E., Julia M. Aguirre, Corey Drake, Tonya G. Bartell, Amy Roth McDuffie, and Mary Q. Foote. "Community Mathematics Exploration Module." In *TeachMath Learning Modules for K–8 Mathematics Methods Courses*, edited by Corey Drake et al. (www .teachmath.info), 2015.

Turner, Erin E., Corey Drake, Amy Roth McDuffie, Julia M. Aguirre, Tonya G. Bartell, and Mary Q. Foote. "Promoting Equity in Mathematics Teacher Preparation: A Framework for Advancing Teacher Learning of Children's Multiple Mathematics Knowledge Bases." *Journal of Mathematics Teacher Education* 15, no. 1 (2012): 67–82.

About the Editors

Sylvia Celedón-Pattichis is professor of bilingual/mathematics education and a Chester C. Travelstead Endowed Faculty Fellow at the University of New Mexico. Her research focuses on linguistic and cultural influences on the teaching and learning of mathematics, particularly with emergent bilinguals; children's mathematical thinking; and the preparation of teachers to work with culturally and linguistically diverse students. She has worked on several projects with teachers, students, and schools that promote equity in mathematics teaching and learning. Recent publications include *Beyond Good Teaching: Advancing Mathematics Education for ELLs* (NCTM 2012) and *Equity within Mathematics Education Research as a Political Act: Moving from Choice to Intentional Collective Responsibility* (2017).

Dorothy Y. White is associate professor of mathematics education in the College of Education at the University of Georgia. Her research focuses on equity and culture in mathematics education by studying the preparation of teachers to teach in culturally diverse classrooms and the development of teacher professional learning communities. She teaches undergraduate and graduate level mathematics methods courses and provides professional development for Pre-K–grade 8 mathematics teachers at the national, state, and local levels. Recent publications include *Cases for Mathematics Teacher Educators: Facilitating Conversations about Inequities in Mathematics Classrooms* (2016) and "Educators Learning from Middle School Students' Views of Mathematical Strengths" (2017).

Marta Civil is professor of mathematics education and the Roy F. Graesser Chair in the Department of Mathematics at The University of Arizona. Her research looks at cultural, social, and language aspects in the teaching and learning of mathematics; connections between in-school and out-of-school mathematics; and parental engagement in mathematics. She has led funded projects working with children, parents, and teachers, with a focus on developing culturally responsive learning environments, particularly with Latina/o communities. Recent publications include "STEM Learning Research through a Funds of Knowledge Lens" (2016); *Common Core State Standards in Mathematics for English Language Learners: Grades K–8* (NCTM 2014); and *Cases for Mathematics Teacher Educators: Facilitating Conversations about Inequities in Mathematics Classrooms* (2016). Civil is also the editor for NCTM's Access and Equity series.